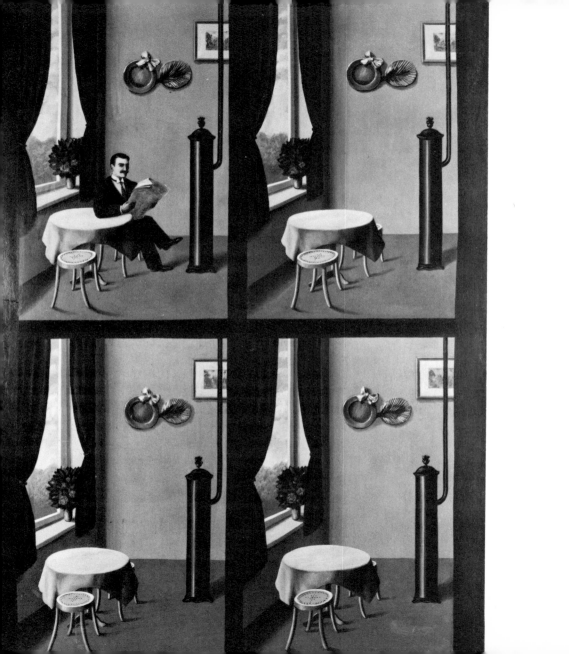

I looked in   a looking glass

hoping to   find myself

but found   you, waiting

LOOKING GLASS

an anthology of contemporary poetry
edited by Eric Williams

EDWARD ARNOLD

First published 1973
by Edward Arnold (Publishers) Ltd
25 Hill Street
London, W1X 8LL

ISBN: 0 7131 1787 7

Printed in Great Britain by
Fletcher & Son Ltd, Norwich

PREFACE

This anthology of contemporary poetry is intended for use primarily with students aged 16–18 in sixth forms and colleges of further education (though I have used many of the poems successfully with younger pupils as well). The poems included here have stimulated vigorous discussion and further reading among the students I have taught, and at the end of this volume I have indicated, tentatively, some lines of approach we have followed. As with my previous anthology, *Dragonsteeth*, great care has been taken to place the poems in an order that will give the anthology unity, each poem commenting and enlarging on the content of those that surround it ; and, again, full use has been made of the double-spread layout and the choice of illustrations to high-light the relation of the poems to one another. In the suggestions for discussion I have also grouped the poems in units that have proved successful in use with my students. The illustrations do more than merely illustrate : they have been chosen for the impact they make in themselves, adding a further dimension to the poems' meaning, and providing a further stimulus for discussion and creative writing.

The poems' chief concern is with people and their relationships—in love, in facing problems like loneliness and old age, and as a community—probing issues that students will feel strongly about and want to discuss further : and I have found that the reading and discussion of these poems encourages students to write poetry themselves. The scope of this anthology, then, is not confined to the 'English' lesson : I envisage it also being used in Humanities and General Studies courses, where non-specialist students will be concerned with what the poems have to *say*, rather than with literary technique. The anthology is also complementary to *People*, exploring some of the crises and conflicts raised there. At the same time this book provides a valuable introduction to the exciting range of poetry now being written, giving a perspective in which an A-Level student can place writers chosen for detailed study.

E.W.

CONTENTS

Man, Animal, Clock of Blood

The animal runs
it eats, it sleeps
it dies
      goes the old song

and then :
the great cold
the night, the dark . . .

In the dark, the man runs
he stumbles, he hurts
  his face, the world is hard on his face, is a she
he is in love with the world

lord of creation, he wears his shoes large
     make way, make way
he does not think of that night
he is warm, he will love her, if only, whenever
      he finds her

if only he could go without eating
if only he could do without sleep
if only he could hold her forever
he need not die
      goes the old song
      in his head

and he keeps on walking and wanting
the beautiful goof, walking and
wanting : make way for the lord
idiot, flower, awkward
        man

ANSELM HOLLO

Out of Unrest

The blue iris, opening at dawn,
startled me out of my mind.
I turned
     away from it
     to the window :

    blue stars burning down,
    lighting the universe
    a moment, then dying
    into the sun's greater light.

Light that is reaching us from stars,
dead a thousand years, was held once
in the huge arms of Andromeda. We see
only memories of starfire—our bodies,
a memory of fathers long dead.
Their voices rush, muffled by distance,
down streams of the blood, opening channels
of first feeling in the flood.

What piece of us is not
striving to get back
to the One Man, is dead.
Who does not know the
dead in the wind and
the dead within would be one
has no way out of time . . .

　　'. . . it does not really exist
　　without unrest; it does not exist
　　for dumb animals.' (Kierkegaard)

But I will not be dumb
nor rest, but celebrate
　　what I am.

It is difficult. There are
so many people I am,
　　obscuring

the one face I would become.

PAUL EVANS

Prayer Before Birth

I am not yet born ; O hear me.
Let not the bloodsucking bat or the rat or the stoat or the
  club-footed ghoul come near me.

I am not yet born, console me.
I fear that the human race may with tall walls wall me,
  with strong drugs dope me, with wise lies lure me,
    on black racks rack me, in blood-baths roll me.

I am not yet born ; provide me
With water to dandle me, grass to grow for me, trees to talk
  to me, sky to sing to me, birds and a white light
    in the back of my mind to guide me.

I am not yet born ; forgive me
For the sins that in me the world shall commit, my words
  when they speak me, my thoughts when they think me,
    my treason engendered by traitors beyond me,
      my life when they murder by means of my
        hands, my death when they live me.

I am not yet born ; rehearse me
In the parts I must play and the cues I must take when
  old men lecture me, bureaucrats hector me, mountains
    frown at me, lovers laugh at me, the white
      waves call me to folly and the desert calls
        me to doom and the beggar refuses
          my gift and my children curse me.

I am not yet born ; O hear me,
Let not the man who is beast or who thinks he is God
  come near me.

I am not yet born ; O fill me
With strength against those who would freeze
  humanity, would dragoon me into a lethal automaton,
    would make me a cog in a machine, a thing with
      one face, a thing, and against all those
        who would dissipate my entirety, would

blow me like thistledown hither and
thither or hither and thither
like water held in the
hands would spill me.

Let them not make me a stone and let them not spill me.
Otherwise kill me.

LOUIS MACNEICE

Narcissus

Narcissus,
You gazed in a pool once and saw
Your own reflection magnified.
But you saw more than this only ;
There was also
The crystalline presence, the glorious loving
Of self and self.
All this Carvaggio also saw
And painted.

Much of our lives is lived
In such vivid gazes,
But it is not enough,
Not enough.
We need to go beyond that translucence
And beyond the delightful waters
See others, see others.

For children, the self is sufficient,
But now, later,
There must be a turning away,
A turning towards another.
Throw a pebble in the stream and then
Look behind you. The world is there.

ELIZABETH JENNINGS

The Ripples

You troubled the still pool of my mind
Like a pebble dropped into it. And I was so
Intent on wondering whose was the hand
And what it was that made these ripples flow
Outwards, questingly, as if to find
Something beyond themselves—how could I know

That into your mind too a stone had dropped ?
It was the laws of motion in the end
That brought us into love. For as they touched
Our ripples hesitated, spread and widened,
Shivered to a singleness, then stopped.
Where now did the waters meet and blend ?

DAVID SUTTON

Passing Through

We had to start from where our parents put us
Until we met in the lists of coming and going.

Where do they begin, attractions, pity,
And when they're finished, where do they go?

Like water that cupped hands cannot hold,
We passed through each other, we changed,
    sometimes

We even disappeared, flowing off elsewhere,
Sucked into porous distances, making gaps

That were wider than geography,
Dried up in the sun of consuming loves.

Walking together through spaces other people have
    filled,
Our edges become hot in the air remembering them.

DOUGLAS DUNN

Mary, Mary Magdalene

*On the south wall of the church of St Mary Magda-
lene at Launceston in Cornwall is a granite figure of
the saint. The children of the town say that a stone
lodged on her back will bring good luck.*

Mary, Mary Magdalene
Lying on the wall,
I throw a pebble on your back.
Will it lie or fall?

Send me down for Christmas
Some stockings and some hose,
And send before the winter's end
A brand-new suit of clothes.

Mary, Mary Magdalene
Under a stony tree,
I throw a pebble on your back.
What will you send me?

> *I'll send you for your Christening
> A woollen robe to wear,
> A shiny cup from which to sup,
> And a name to bear.*

Mary, Mary Magdalene
Lying cool as snow,
What will you be sending me
When to school I go?

> *I'll send a pencil and a pen
> That write both clean and neat,
> And I'll send to the schoolmaster
> A tongue that's kind and sweet.*

Mary, Mary Magdalene
Lying in the sun,
What will you be sending me
Now I'm twenty-one?

> *I'll send you down a locket
> As silver as your skin,
> And I'll send you a lover
> To fit a gold key in.*

Mary, Mary Magdalene
Underneath the spray,
What will you be sending me
On my wedding-day?

> *I'll send you down some blossom,
> Some ribbons and some lace,
> And for the bride a veil to hide
> The blushes on her face.*

Mary, Mary Magdalene
Whiter than the swan,
Tell me what you'll send me
Now my good man's dead and gone?

> *I'll send to you a single bed
> On which you must lie,
> And pillows bright where tears may light
> That fall from your eye.*

Mary, Mary Magdalene
Now nine months are done,
What will you be sending me
For my little son?

> *I'll send you for your baby
> A lucky stone, and small,
> To throw to Mary Magdalene
> Lying on the wall.*

CHARLES CAUSLEY

Reported Missing

Can you give me a precise description?
Said the policeman. Her lips, I told him,
Were soft. Could you give me, he said, pencil
Raised, a metaphor? Soft as an open mouth,
I said. Were there any noticeable
Peculiarities? he asked. Her hair hung
Heavily, I said. Any particular
Colour? he said. I told him I could recall
Little but its distinctive scent. What do
You mean, he asked, by distinctive? It had
The smell of a woman's hair, I said. Where
Were you? he asked. Closer than I am to
Anyone at present, I said; level with
Her mouth, level with her eyes. Her eyes?
He said. What about her eyes? There were two,
I said, both black. It has been established,
He said, that eyes cannot, outside common
Usage, be black; are you implying that
Violence was used? Only the gentle
Hammer blow of her kisses, the scent
Of her breath, the . . . Quite, said the policeman,
Standing. But I regret that we know of
No one answering to such a description.

BARRY COLE

The Worst of All Loves

Where do they go, the faces, the people seen
In glances and longed for, who smile back
Wondering where the next kiss is coming from?

They are seen suddenly, from the top decks of buses,
On railway platforms at the tea machine,
When the sleep of travelling makes us look for them.

A whiff of perfume, an eye, a hat, a shoe,
Bring back vague memories of names,
Thingummy, that bloke, what's-her-name.

What great thing have I lost, that faces in a crowd
Should make me look at them for one I know,
What are faces that they must be looked for?

But there's one face, seen only once,
A fragment of a crowd. I know enough of her.
That face makes me dissatisfied with myself.

Those we secretly love, who never know of us,
What happens to them? Only this is known.
They will never meet us suddenly in pleasant rooms.

DOUGLAS DUNN

Outside the Gates of Eden

A leaden day, a strange town
And the lights against me.
It was by chance I was to see
Her leaning in a shop doorway. Her frown
Suggesting a boredom to come, she waited
To begin a Monday already mocking
Her week-end pretensions,
The seam of her temper awry as her stocking.

She looked up, and catching me looking, smiled.
I noticed her eyes, wistful, the curls
Of her hair piled,
The high cheeks of those Botticelli girls.
Even her dank mac could not disguise
The warm weight of her beauty.

For a moment we were one in surprise
Of that neat world where
Love is compassion and bodies
For pleasure, forgetful how rare
The escape from shoddy
Routine, duties or plain necessity.
Only the lights changed when I moved with the
traffic.

JOHN COTTON

At Lunchtime A Story of Love

When the busstopped suddenly to avoid
damaging a mother and child in the road, the
younglady in the green hat sitting opposite
was thrown across me, and not being one to
miss an opportunity i started to makelove
with all my body.

   At first she resisted saying that it
was tooearly in the morning and toosoon
after breakfast and that anyway she found
me repulsive. But when i explained that
this being a nuclearage, the world was going
to end at lunchtime, she tookoff her
greenhat, put her busticket in her pocket
and joined in the exercise.

The buspeople, and therewere many of
them, were shockedandsurprised and amused-
andannoyed, but when the word got around
that the world was coming to an end at lunchtime, they put their pride in their pockets
with their bustickets and madelove one with
the other. And even the busconductor, being
over, climbed into the cab and struck up
some sort of relationship with the driver.

   Thatnight, on the bus coming home,
wewere all alittle embarrassed, especially me
and the younglady in the greenhat, and we
all started to say in different ways howhasty
and foolish we had been. Butthen, always
having been a bitofalad, i stood up and
said it was a pity that the world didn't nearly
end every lunchtime and that we could always
pretend. And then it happened . . .

   Quick asa crash we all changed partners
and soon the bus was aquiver with white
mothballbodies doing naughty things.

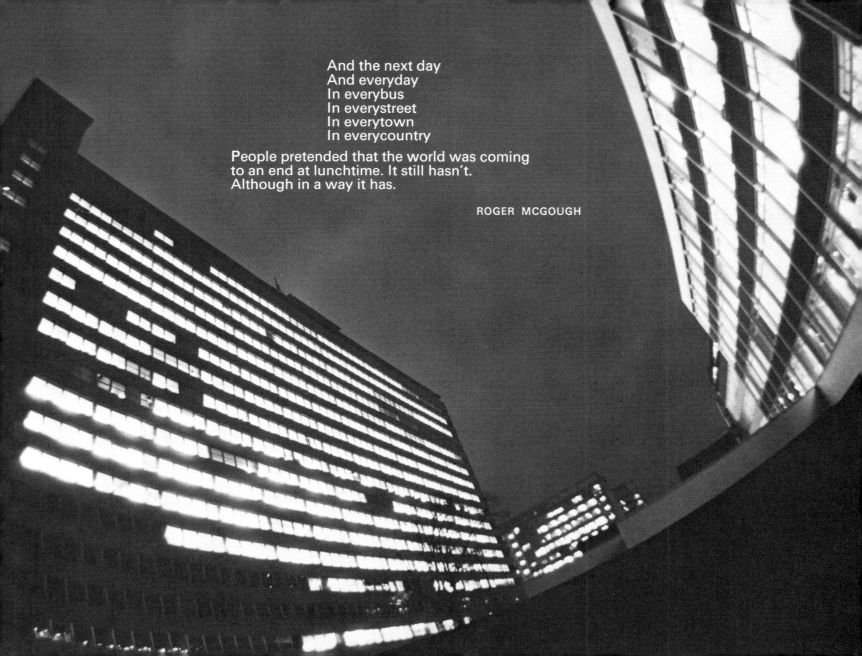

And the next day
And everyday
In everybus
In everystreet
In everytown
In everycountry

People pretended that the world was coming
to an end at lunchtime. It still hasn't.
Although in a way it has.

ROGER MCGOUGH

Parlour-Piece

With love so like fire they dared not
Let it out into strawy small talk ;
With love so like a flood they dared not
Let out a trickle lest the whole crack,

These two sat speechlessly :
Pale cool tea in tea-cups chaperoned
Stillness, silence, the eyes
Where fire and flood strained.

TED HUGHES

Hesitant

He sees beyond her face another face.
It is the one he wants.
He stares at it in amazement ;
There is nothing anywhere quite like it.
There is nothing else that's wanted.

She sees beyond his face another face.
It stares at her in amazement.
She stares back, equally amazed.
Just why, she can't quite answer.
She simply wants it.

These faces have been waiting now
A long time to be introduced.
If only the faces in front
Would do something about it.

BRIAN PATTEN

Incident

I look across the table and think
(fiery with love)
Ask me, go on, ask me
to do something impossible,
something freakishly useless,
something unimaginable and inimitable

like making a finger break into blossom
or walking for half an hour in twenty minutes
or remembering tomorrow.

I will you to ask it.
But all you say is
Will you give me a cigarette?
And I smile and,
returning to the marvellous world
of possibility,
I give you one
with a hand that trembles
with a human trembling.

NORMAN MACCAIG

The Rag Doll to the Heedless Child

I love you
with my linen heart.

You cannot
know how these

rigid, lumpy arms
shudder in your grasp,

or what
tears dam up against

these blue eye-smudges at
your capriciousness.

At night I watch you sleep;
you'll never know

how I thrust my face
into the stream

of your warm breath;
and how

love-words choke me behind
this sewn-up mouth.

DAVID HARSENT

Pomander

pomander
open pomander
open poem and her
open poem and him
open poem and hymn
hymn and hymen leander
high man pen meander
o pen poem me and her
pen me poem me and him
om mane padme hum
pad me home panda hand
open up o holy panhandler
ample panda pen or bamboo pond
ponder a bonny poem pomander opener
open banned peon penman hum and banter
open hymn and pompom band and panda hamper
o i am a pen open man or happener
i am open manner happener
happy are we open
poem and a pom
poem and a panda
poem and aplomb

EDWIN MORGAN

Jenny

WORDS
WORDS
WORDS
WORDS
WORDS
WORDS
WORDS
WORDS
WORDS
WORDS
WORDS she once said, 'I love you
WORDS
WORDS
WORDS
WORDS
WORDS
WORDS
WORDS
WORDS
WORDS
WORDS
WORDS
WORDS I cannot live without you'
WORDS
WORDS
WORDS
WORDS
WORDS
WORDS
WORDS
WORDS
WORDS
WORDS
WORDS like they do in the films.

GERALD ASHBY

First Love

That was her beginning, an apparition
of rose in the unbreathed airs of his love,
her heart revealed by the wash of summer
sprung from her childhood's shallow stream.

Then it was that she put up her hair,
inscribed her eyes with a look of grief,
while her limbs grew as curious as coral branches,
her breast full of secrets.

But the boy, confused in his day's desire,
was searching for herons, his fingers bathed
in the green of walnuts, or watching at night
the Great Bear spin from the maypole star.

It was then that he paused in the death of a game,
felt the hook of her hair on his swimming throat,
saw her mouth at large in the dark river
flushed like a salmon.

But he covered his face and hid his joy
in a wild-goose web of false directions,
and hunted the woods for eggs and glow-worms,
for rabbits tasteless as moss.

And she walked in fields where the crocuses
branded her feet, and mares' tails sprang
from the prancing lake, and the salty grasses
surged round her stranded body.

LAURIE LEE

Seascape

gulls kiss the sun
and you walk on the beach
afraid of the tide

from the sea's warm belly
a lobster crawls to
see if we've gone

but mouths still talk
and finding out my lips
I say to you :

'lie silently
and stretch out your arms
like seaweed strangled by the wind'

out of a seashell
a sandcrab pokes his head
and sniffs the salt wind

now afraid we sit in silence
and watching the sun go down
I ask you your name

BRIAN PATTEN

From *A Humament*

236 A HUMAN DOCUMENT.

sometimes silence, sometimes

breaks

words so full of

her sad to-night.

the sad

horizon of

sea

hours

she spent with

her sadness

on the beach,

This Day . . .

This day is like a gull that glides
On polished air, its white breast dipped in
A fire of voices. The image glows
Then smoulders on the darkening sea.

Today we shall speak of life and
Perhaps forget to live it, drifting
Lazily on our separate streams, feeling
The hot air furrow us apart.

And beneath the sun we lie still to
Stare warily at each other, wondering if
The hand's caress will scratch and maim,
Holding trust tight in a fist of suspicion.

We circle the day, controlling its motion,
Afraid to yield place to another's greed.
The eye turns to amber, hardening its gleam,
Turning desire into a dull, steady flap.

Spinning slowly, we edge our ways
Into dizziness, falling together at last.
And over our recoil a gull still
Floats, serene on the polished air.

ERIC WILLIAMS

TOM PHILLIPS

The Love Day

April, and young women glorify their flesh.
Their blushes warm their lovers' eyes.

The frisky toughs discard their heavy jackets,
Put on dark, sparse muscle-shirts.

Youth walks in couples nervous to cool bedrooms.
Some learn that love is not bad or permanent.

The ruffians are soft with their girlfriends.
They smile, keep their voices down, park their
    motorbikes.

Spring, the fugitives come to a stop here,
The thrush muffles its voice under the blossom,

Young husbands notice the flower shops,
The old men kiss their wives and long for children.

It only lasts a day. After it, the insects come out.
Tender hands and mouths go back to eating.

DOUGLAS DUNN

Rupert Hears Gruff Voices

we love
       don't we
you think love
can survive don't you

love's still alive

    it's life

   is rebirth

loving is to give

     share
      help
       to grow
it's like flying
to another world
in a new silver plane
two people holding hands
       across no void

I love you
  —walk
along with me

we don't

non-existent

dead

is death

suicide

to take

use
destroy
a way we swallow each other
kind of springtime cannibalism
grab a palatable mate
you start to eat
        and she
eats you   you share
separate meals together

go away
nobody plays that game
anymore

MAURICE COCKRILL

The Whitsun Weddings

That Whitsun, I was late getting away :
    Not till about
One-twenty on the sunlit Saturday
Did my three-quarters-empty train pull out,
All windows down, all cushions hot, all sense
of being in a hurry gone. We ran
Behind the backs of houses, crossed a street
Of blinding windscreens, smelt the fish-dock ;
    thence
The river's level drifting breadth began,
Where sky and Lincolnshire and water meet.

All afternoon, through the tall heat that slept
    For miles inland,
A slow and stopping curve southwards we kept.
Wide farms went by, short-shadowed cattle, and
Canals with floatings of industrial froth ;
A hothouse flashed uniquely ; hedges dipped
And rose ; and now and then a smell of grass
Displaced the reek of buttoned carriage-cloth
Until the next town, new and nondescript,
Approached with acres of dismantled cars.

At first, I didn't notice what a noise
    The weddings made
Each station that we stopped at : sun destroys
The interest of what's happening in the shade,
And down the long cool platforms whoops and
    skirls
I took for porters larking with the mails
And went on reading. Once we started, though,
We passed them, grinning and pomaded, girls
In parodies of fashion, heels and veils,
All posed irresolutely, watching us go,

As if out on the end of an event
    Waving goodbye
To something that survived it. Struck, I leant
More promptly out next time, more curiously,

And saw it all again in different terms :
The fathers with broad belts under their suits
And seamy foreheads : mothers loud and fat ;
An uncle shouting smut ; and then the perms,
The nylon gloves and jewellery-substitutes,
The lemons, mauves, and olive-ochres that

Marked off the girls unreally from the rest.
    Yes, from cafés
And banquet-halls up yards, and bunting-dressed
Coach-party annexes, the wedding-days
Were coming to an end. All down the line
Fresh couples climbed aboard ; the rest stood round ;
The last confetti and advice were thrown,
And, as we moved, each face seemed to define
Just what it saw departing : children frowned
At something dull ; fathers had never known

Success so huge and wholly farcical ;
The women shared
The secret like a happy funeral ;
While girls, gripping their handbags tighter, stared
At a religious wounding. Free at last,
And loaded with the sum of all they saw,
We hurried towards London, shuffling gouts of
    steam.
Now fields were building-plots, and poplars cast
Long shadows over major roads, and for
Some fifty minutes, that in time would seem

Just long enough to settle hats and say
    I nearly died
A dozen marriages got under way.
They watched the landscape, sitting side by side
—An Odeon went past, a cooling tower,
And someone running up to bowl—and none
Thought of the others they would never meet
Or how their lives would all contain this hour.
I thought of London spread out in the sun,
Its postal districts packed like squares of wheat :

There we were aimed. And as we raced across
    Bright knots of rail
Past standing Pullmans, walls of blackened moss
Came close, and it was nearly done, this frail
Travelling coincidence ; and what it held
Stood ready to be loosed with all the power
That being changed can give. We slowed again,
And as the tightened brakes took hold, there swelled
A sense of falling, like an arrow-shower
Sent out of sight, somewhere becoming rain.

PHILIP LARKIN

Anemones for Miss Austen

Indeed a sweet and knowing lady,
quietly scribbling away her time ;
the geographer of a gentle clime
where only the lanes were shady,
the poor kept decently out of sight,
and the neat old-fashioned carriages
manoeuvred the country marriages,
where the curates came off worst, as well they might.

The cool young heroines got their men,
and in due time were suitably wed.
None of the details escaped her pen.

And yet, somehow she never quite said
a word about what happened then,
how they managed with breakfast or bed.

BERNARD BERGONZI

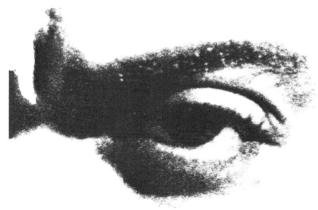

As Others See Us

She finding on his lips
sour champagne, and he
on her hair confetti,
they enter that eclipse

the novels promise. She
in his eyes, he in hers,
melt as the moon devours
the sun. They do not see—

until a sixth raw sense
nags them to consciousness—
the eye against the glass
cold as a camera lens.

Sickened, they see in this
a creature double-backed
disturbed in a gross act.
The eye blinks, vanishes :

but still the staring pane
holds like a negative
her Adam and his Eve
unparadised again.

JON STALLWORTHY

Horoscope

Eyes striving to hold the future
Find joy softened by tears.
Doubt flickers its old film,
The images blurred in the stillness
Of our gaze.

Silent, our hands speak for us,
Trace the lines on which our lives
Merge, while our mouths close on
The eloquence of a love that need
Only say :

'We are no longer apart.
The world is spun on our
Single breath. Your warmth is
Mine now. Your sorrow wears
My smile.'

ERIC WILLIAMS

Love Poem

I live in you, you live in me ;
We are two gardens haunted by each other.
Sometimes I cannot find you there,
There is only the swing creaking, that you have
    just left,
Or your favourite book beside the sundial.

DOUGLAS DUNN

Absence

I visited the place where we last met.
Nothing was changed, the gardens were well-tended
The fountains sprayed their usual steady jet ;
There was no sign that anything had ended
And nothing to instruct me to forget.

The thoughtless birds that shook out of the trees,
Singing an ecstasy I could not share,
Played cunning in my thoughts. Surely in these
Pleasures there could not be a pain to bear
Or any discord shake the level breeze.

It was because the place was just the same
That made your absence seem a savage force,
For under all the gentleness there came
An earthquake tremor : fountain, birds and grass
Were shaken by my thinking of your name.

ELIZABETH JENNINGS

Love Poem

your total absence
rehearsal of my death

in this game
there is no substitute
all symbol gone
the knife flicks home
for real—

your silence
     spreads like water
          in an empty room

limp flowers
     in cellophane
          your gift
their scent rises
     a thin column
          leaning towards me

black trees
     barricade the sky
each morning
     we are ambushed
          by birds

your skull echoes

an inexhaustible fountain
          of sound

FRANCES HOROVITZ

At Night

I think at night my hands are mad,
for they follow the irritant texture of darkness
continually carving the sad leaf of your mouth
in the thick black bark of sleep.

And my finger-joints are quick with insanity,
springing with lost amazement
through a vast waste of dreams
and forming frames of desire
around the thought of your eyes.

By day, the print of your body
is like a stroke of sun on my hands,
and the choir of your blood
goes chanting incessantly
through the echoing channels of my wrists.

But I am lost in my hut
when the stars are out,
for my palms have a catlike faculty of sight,
and the surface of every minute
is a swinging image of you.

LAURIE LEE

Telescope

The army advanced by night
at dawn the pearl grey of the sea
a large bird flying too slowly   I may be tired now
but lying in bed watching thin white clouds
passing through the window in a clear sky
Your smile is inside me   I wait
In this morning stillness everything seems at peace
the white sheets   the delicate ring of my watch
ticking in a bare white room overlooking the sea
One direction the harbour and the green band of
waves
below the horizon—the other the heavy roundness
of the hills, the darker green of the Downs
The army subsides and melts like the night at dawn
—it's in the past now. Thoughts of you glow inside
me.
A pale late winter sunshine floods the whole
landscape
in a harsh white light and so makes it
look totally bare—the word 'naked' can even be
used now—
and this same air of nakedness in the sunlight
is like an announcement of the coming spring
The comparison expands and I see this all as a
reflection of your coming return that I now wait for
and how I lie here this morning thinking of you
Far from the shore a small cargo boat presses on
—from here its progress looks painfully slow
but this doesn't matter   neither I nor the boat's
crew
can be ruffled with such good things so obviously
in store for us

LEE HARWOOD

Travelling Between Places

Leaving nothing and nothing ahead ;
when you stop for the evening
the sky will be in ruins,

when you hear late birds
with tired throats singing
think how good it is that they

knowing you were coming,
stayed up late to greet you
who travels between places

when the late afternoon
drifts into the woods, when
nothing matters specially.

BRIAN PATTEN

The Lane

Last night, the moon close and touchable,
so richly yellow.
Now, late afternoon,
it ghosts the sky like melting ice.
We scrunch the lane.

He stands, eating.
His eyes slide to fix us when we pass.

Abrupt, we turn.
A cling of briars
gives to a track anciently rutted.
The tut-tut-tut begins
of his blades whittling the next excess.

The pressure of your hand in my hand—
small round warmth, a charm
pressed into a grip.

BRIAN JONES

When You Go

When you go,
if you go,
and I should want to die,
there's nothing I'd be saved by
more than the time
you fell asleep in my arms
in a trust so gentle
I let the darkening room
drink up the evening, till
rest, or the new rain
lightly roused you awake.
I asked if you heard the rain in your dream
and half dreaming still you only said, I love you

EDWIN MORGAN

You Become a Star

Your face so near   your body
at the sea's edge   many continents
away in the distance   the whole shoreline
vibrating   the blue grey sky at night

A single star   through the large window
bareness
nakedness   in the sky   in you & I
the star   the nakedness   'is the work of God'
leaving the very essence   so pure

No matter what the trigger on this occasion
that fires the lightning bolt   the flash
in our bodies   it illuminates the same
landscape

The night is as quiet   your sureness
our bodies shining stars   & beyond
& within   the physical positions no more
than where or what we want

Your return   through the winter
the orange lights of the harbour seen in the distance
I await you patiently   the tide drags the shingle
down the beach   then returns it

So close even now   the shingle
dragged by the waves
fixed in the night sky   as clean & fresh
small pebbles washed by the sea

the night so quiet

LEE HARWOOD

At Four O'Clock in the Morning

As all is temporary and is changeable,
So in this bed my love you lie,
Temporary beyond imaginings;
Trusting and certain, in present time you rest,
A world completed.

Yet already are the windows freaked with dawn;
Shrill song reminds
Each of a separate knowledge;
Shrill light might make of love
A weight both false and monstrous.

So hush; enough words are used:
We know how blunt can grow such phrases as
Only children use without
Awareness of their human weight.

There is no need to impose upon feelings
Yesterday's echo.
I love you true enough;
Beyond this, nothing is now expected.

BRIAN PATTEN

Touch

You are already
asleep. I lower
myself in next to
you, my skin slightly
numb with the restraint
of habits, the patina of
self, the black frost
of outsideness, so that even
unclothed it is
a resilient chilly
hardness, a superficially
malleable, dead
rubbery texture.

You are a mound
of bedclothes, where the cat
in sleep braces
its paws against your
calf through the blankets,
and kneads each paw in turn.

Meanwhile and slowly
I feel a is it
my own warmth surfacing or
the ferment of your whole
body that in darkness beneath
the cover is stealing
bit by bit to break
down that chill.

You turn and
hold me tightly, do
you know who
I am or am I
your mother or
the nearest human being to
hold on to in a
dreamed pogrom.

What I, now loosened,
sink into is an old
big place, it is
there already, for
you are already
there, and the cat
got there before you, yet
it is hard to locate.
What is more, the place is
not found but seeps
from our touch in
continuous creation, dark
enclosing cocoon round
ourselves alone, dark
wide realm where we
walk with everyone.

THOM GUNN

Bodies

At home now   the first grey
in the hollows,   morning in
the grass,   in the brick
I hold you sleeping

and see last night
a bang the back door opens
holding your arm you
white say don't
be frightened smiling

your loving mouth
but white you are white

on a window a
window was it
into the flesh of your arm :
hung in the lab
in the hum of a
ship's hold,   no-one
to hear or help you

O you are stitched and
safe now, my fingers

feel you, I can
taste the oil in your skin, your salty hair

knowing your blue
strings where the blood is
wanting you safe in
hard and shining steel
or tough as mineral, so
even a thin spirit of you
could be unkillable

ELAINE FEINSTEIN

somewhere i have never travelled, gladly beyond

somewhere i have never travelled,gladly beyond
any experience,your eyes have their silence :
in your most frail gesture are things which enclose
me,
or which i cannot touch because they are too near

your slightest look easily will unclose me
though i have closed myself as fingers,
you open always petal by petal myself as Spring
opens
(touching skilfully,mysteriously)her first rose

or if your wish be to close me,i and
my life will shut very beautifully,suddenly,
as when the heart of this flower imagines
the snow carefully everywhere descending ;

nothing which we are to perceive in this world
equals
the power of your intense fragility :whose texture
compels me with the colour of its countries,
rendering death and forever with each breathing

(i do not know what it is about you that closes
and opens;only something in me understands
the voice of your eyes is deeper than all roses)
nobody,not even the rain,has such small hands

e. e. cummings

Part of Plenty

When she carries food to the table and stoops down
—Doing this out of love—and lays soup with its good
Tickling smell, or fry winking from the fire
And I look up, perhaps from a book I am reading
Or other work : there is an importance of beauty
Which can't be accounted for by there and then,
And attacks me, but not separately from the welcome
Of the food, or the grace of her arms.

When she puts a sheaf of tulips in a jug
And pours in water and presses to one side
The upright stems and leaves that you hear creak,
Or loosens them, or holds them up to show me,
So that I see the tangle of their necks and cups
With the curls of her hair, and the body they are held
Against, and the stalk of the small waist rising
And flowering in the shape of breasts ;
Whether in the bringing of the flowers or the food
She offers plenty, and is part of plenty,
And whether I see her stooping, or leaning with the
flowers,
What she does is ages old, and she is not simply,
No, but lovely in that way.

BERNARD SPENCER

Happiness

I asked professors who teach the meaning of life to tell me what is happiness.
And I went to famous executives who boss the work of thousands of men.
They all shook their heads and gave me a smile as though I was trying to fool with them.
And then one Sunday I wandered out along the Desplaines river
And I saw a crowd of Hungarians under the trees with their women
and children and a keg of beer and an accordion.

CARL SANDBURG

The Wife's Tale

When I had spread it all on linen cloth
Under the hedge, I called them over.
The hum and gulp of the thresher ran down
And the big belt slewed to a standstill, straw
Hanging undelivered in the jaws.
There was such quiet that I heard their boots
Crunching the stubble twenty yards away.

He lay down and said 'Give these fellows theirs.
I'm in no hurry,' plucking grass in handfuls
And tossing it in the air. 'That looks well.'
(He nodded at my white cloth on the grass.)
'I declare a woman could lay out a field
Though boys like us have little call for cloths.'
He winked, then watched me as I poured a cup
And buttered the thick slices that he likes.
'It's threshing better than I thought, and mind
It's good clean seed. Away over there and look.'
Always this inspection has to be made
Even when I don't know what to look for.

But I ran my hand in the half-filled bags
Hooked to the slots. It was hard as shot,
Innumerable and cool. The bags gaped
Where the chutes ran back to the stilled drum
And forks were stuck at angles in the ground
As javelins might mark lost battlefields.
I moved between them back across the stubble.

They lay in the ring of their own crusts and dregs
Smoking and saying nothing. 'There's good yield,
Isn't there?'—as proud as if he were the land itself—
'Enough for crushing and for sowing both.'
And that was it. I'd come and he had shown me
So I belonged no further to the work.
I gathered cups and folded up the cloth
And went. But they still kept their ease,
Spread out, unbuttoned, grateful, under the trees.

SEAMUS HEANEY

Trio

Coming up Buchanan Street, quickly, on a sharp winter evening
a young man and two girls, under the Christmas lights—
The young man carries a new guitar in his arms,
the girl on the inside carries a very young baby,
and the girl on the outside carries a chihuahua.
And the three of them are laughing, their breath rises
in a cloud of happiness, and as they pass
the boy says, 'Wait till he sees this but !'
The chihuahua has a tiny Royal Stewart tartan coat like a teapot-holder,
the baby in its white shawl is all bright eyes and mouth like favours in a fresh sweet cake,
the guitar swells out under its milky plastic cover, tied at the neck with
            silver tinsel tape and a brisk sprig of mistletoe.
Orphean sprig ! Melting baby ! Warm chihuahua !
The vale of tears is powerless before you.
Whether Christ is born, or is not born, you
put paid to fate, it abdicates
                        under the Christmas lights.
Monsters of the year
go blank, are scattered back,
can't bear this march of three.

—And the three have passed, vanished in the crowd
(yet not vanished, for in their arms they wind
the life of men and beasts, and music,
laughter ringing them round like a guard)
at the end of this winter's day.

EDWIN MORGAN

Men of Terry Street

They come in at night, leave in the early morning.
I hear their footsteps, the ticking of bicycle chains,
Sudden blasts of motorcycles, whimpering of vans.
Somehow I am either in bed, or the curtains are
drawn.

This masculine invisibility makes gods of them,
A pantheon of boots and overalls.
But when you see them, home early from work
Or at their Sunday leisure, they are too tired

And bored to look long at comfortably.
It hurts to see their faces, too sad or too jovial.
They quicken their step at the smell of cooking,
They hold up their children and sing to them.

DOUGLAS DUNN

Morning Song

Love set you going like a fat gold watch.
The midwife slapped your footsoles, and your bald cry
Took its place among the elements.

Our voices echo, magnifying your arrival. New statue.
In a drafty museum, your nakedness
Shadows our safety. We stand round blankly as walls.

I'm no more your mother
Than the cloud that distils a mirror to reflect its own slow
Effacement at the wind's hand.

All night your moth-breath
Flickers among the flat pink roses. I wake to listen:
A far sea moves in my ear.

One cry, and I stumble from bed, cow-heavy and floral
In my Victorian nightgown.
Your mouth opens clean as a cat's. The window square

Whitens and swallows its dull stars. And now you try
Your handful of notes;
The clear vowels rise like balloons.

SYLVIA PLATH

Human Affection

Mother, I love you so,
Said the child; I love you more than I know.
She laid her head on her mother's arm,
And the love between them kept them warm.

STEVIE SMITH

At Seven a Son

In cold weather on a
garden swing, his legs
in Wellingtons rising over
the winter rose trees

he sits serenely
smiling like a Thai
his coat open, his gloves
sewn to the flapping sleeves

his thin knees working
with his arms
folded about the
metal struts

as he flies up
(his hair like long
black leaves) he
lies back freely

astonished in
sunshine as serious
as a stranger he is
a bird in his own thought.

ELAINE FEINSTEIN

Prayer

In the absence of father or god
bless this son

That his eye will know the details of our lives one day
that created him—

not in the white bitter light
of the empty temple
                    wind, stone or myth

But in the bargain
he must make with his heart
to free himself of all fears not his own
                              not kin to his cry

That his temple be filled
with people and beasts
he can trust without taming

That the horns and water of his birth
guide him through the two worlds

belief in self
belief in things

And finally, give him the nerve
to face his own failure
                         the darker face
behind the face in the mirror

which is his substance, all else being ghost.

DAVID WEVILL

Rising Five

'I'm rising five,' he said,
'Not four', and little coils of hair
Un-clicked themselves upon his head.
His spectacles, brimful of eyes to stare
At me and the meadow, reflected cones of light
Above his toffee-buckled cheeks. He'd been alive
Fifty-six months or perhaps a week more :
                                        not four,
But rising five.

Around him in the field the cells of spring
Bubbled and doubled ; buds unbuttoned ; shoot
And stem shook out the creases from their frills,
And every tree was swilled with green.
It was the season after blossoming,
Before the forming of the fruit :
                            not May,
But rising June.

                    And in the sky
The dust dissected the tangential light :
                                not day,
But rising night ;
                not now,
But rising soon.

The new buds push the old leaves from the bough.
We drop our youth behind us like a boy
Throwing away his toffee-wrappers. We never see the flower,
But only the fruit in the flower ; never the fruit,
But only the rot in the fruit. We look for the marriage bed
In the baby's cradle, we look for the grave in the bed :
                                    not living,
But rising dead.

NORMAN NICHOLSON

Mirror

I am silver and exact. I have no preconceptions.
Whatever I see I swallow immediately
Just as it is, unmisted by love or dislike.
I am not cruel, only truthful—
The eye of a little god, four-cornered.
Most of the time I meditate on the opposite wall.

It is pink, with speckles. I have looked at it so long
I think it is a part of my heart. But it flickers.
Faces and darkness separate us over and over.

Now I am a lake. A woman bends over me,
Searching my reaches for what she really is.
Then she turns to those liars, the candles or the
moon.

I see her back, and reflect it faithfully.
She rewards me with tears and an agitation of hands.
I am important to her. She comes and goes.
Each morning it is her face that replaces the darkness.
In me she has drowned a young girl, and in me an old woman
Rises toward her day after day, like a terrible fish.

SYLVIA PLATH

Old Woman

So much she caused she cannot now account for
As she stands watching day return, the cool
Walls of the house moving towards the sun.
She puts some flowers in a vase and thinks
    'There is not much I can arrange
In here and now, but flowers are suppliant

As children never were. And love is now
A flicker of memory, my body is
My own entirely. When I lie at night
I gather nothing now into my arms,
    No child or man, and where I live
Is what remains when men and children go.

Yet she owns more than residue of lives
That she has marked and altered. See how she
Warns time from too much touching her possessions
    By keeping flowers fed by polishing
        Her fine old silver. Gratefully
She sees her own glance printed on grandchildren.

Drawing the curtains back and opening windows
Every morning now, she feels her years
Grow less and less. Time puts no burden on
Her now she does not need to measure it.
        It is acceptance she arranges
And her own life she places in the vase.

ELIZABETH JENNINGS

Grandfather

They brought him in on a stretcher from the world,
Wounded but humorous. And he soon recovered—
Boiler-rooms, row upon row of gantries rolled
Away to reveal the landscape of a childhood
Only he can recapture. Even on cold
Mornings he is up at six with a block of wood
Or a box of nails, discreetly up to no good
Or banging round the house like a four-year-old—
Never there when you call. But after dark
You hear his great boots thumping in the hall
And in he comes, as cute as they come. Each night
His shrewd eyes bolt the door and set the clock
Against the future, then his light goes out—
Nothing escapes him. He escapes us all.

DEREK MAHON

Two Grandad Poems

Bucket

everyevening after tea
grandad would take his bucket for a walk

An empty bucket

When I asked him why
he said because it was easier to carry
than a full one

grandad had
an answer
for everything

Railings

towards the end of his tether
grandad
at the drop of a hat
would paint the railings

overnight
we became famous
allover the neighbourhood
for our smart railings

(and our dirty hats)

ROGER MCGOUGH

Two Clocks

There was a clock in Grandad's house :
black, gold-numbered,
and a three-foot pendulum.
I'd hear it tick out endless Christmasses,
fingering patches on the green velvet.

Such splendour. *His* chair.
His knife. *His* fork. 'Wait !'
Grandma would say,
'till your father gets in !'
Twisting my mother to a girl again.

Revenge needs time. 'That junk,'
my mother said,
and burned the clock,
the velvet, the Blessed Are the Pure in Heart
in red and gold behind the bed.

And brought him back to live with us,
where bleak electric hands swirled gently,
slicing her days and his
into thin fragments.

JOHN DANIEL

My Grandmother

She kept an antique shop—or it kept her.
Among Apostle spoons and Bristol glass,
The faded silks, the heavy furniture,
She watched her own reflection in the brass
Salvers and silver bowls, as if to prove
Polish was all, there was no need of love.

And I remember how I once refused
To go out with her, since I was afraid.
It was perhaps a wish not to be used
Like antique objects. Though she never said
That she was hurt, I still could feel the guilt
Of that refusal, guessing how she felt.

Later, too frail to keep a shop, she put
All her best things in one long narrow room,
The place smelt old, of things too long kept shut,
The smell of absences where shadows come
That can't be polished. There was nothing then
To give her own reflection back again.

And when she died I felt no grief at all,
Only the guilt of what I once refused.
I walked into her room among the tall
Sideboards and cupboards—things she never used
But needed ; and no finger-marks were there,
Only the new dust falling through the air.

ELIZABETH JENNINGS

The Hospital in Winter

A dark bell leadens the hour,
    The three o'clock
Light falls amber across a tower.

Below, green-railed within a wall
    Of coral brick,
Stretches the borough hospital

Monstrous with smells that cover death,
    White gauze tongues,
Cold-water-pipes of pain, glass breath,

Porcelain, blood, black rubber tyres;
    And in the yards
Plane-trees and slant telephone-wires.

On benches squat the afraid and cold
    Hour after hour.
Chains of windows snarl with gold.

Far off, beyond the engine-sheds,
    Motionless trucks
Grow ponderous, their rotting reds

Deepening towards night; from windows
    Bathrobed men
Watch the horizon flare as the light goes.

Smoke whispers across the town,
    High panes are bleak;
Pink of coral sinks to brown;
A dark bell brings the dark down.

ROY FISHER

Visiting Hour

The hospital smell
combs my nostrils
as they go bobbing along

green and yellow corridors.

What seems a corpse
is trundled into a lift and vanishes
heavenward.

I will not feel, I will not
feel, until
I have to.

Nurses walk lightly, swiftly,
here and up and down and there,
their slender waists miraculously
carrying their burden
of so much pain, so
many deaths, their eyes
still clear after
so many farewells.

Ward 7. She lies
in a white cave of forgetfulness.
A withered hand
trembles on its stalk. Eyes move
behind eyelids too heavy
to raise. Into an arm wasted
of colour a glass fang is fixed,
not guzzling but giving.
And between her and me
distance shrinks till there is none left
but the distance of pain that neither she nor I
can cross.

She smiles a little at this
black figure in her white cave
who clumsily rises
in the round swimming waves of a bell
and dizzily goes off, leaving behind only
books that will not be read
and fruitless fruits.

NORMAN MACCAIG

Memorial

I visited your grave
too often in dreams
while you were still alive

Now I do not want to touch
the real body and the real grass
see the real trees

                 Because
your voice will begin to describe
the leaves, the ladybugs
roots as they are
                 the germ of wind
that reaches you
flowers, your neighbours' names

the same voice
that claimed and exclaimed so often
such things, your eyes
                 quicker than mine
                   still quicker than mine

DAVID WEVILL

With Decorum

I lay down and having
died, gave my instructions : they
filled the room with
balloons and streamers, cherubim at the four
corners of the ceiling blowing their bright bugles—
laid me on a carved catafalque, in an
embroidered robe
crusted with emeralds ; doctor and
priest in black mantles ;
inconsolable women. Trundling of
wheels, the en-
tire building moves to the cemetery. Seagulls are
crying at the shut window. The ba-
lloons joggle.

Grave by a Holm-Oak

You lie there, Anna,
In your grave now,
Under a snow-sky,
You lie there now.

Where have the dead gone ?
Where do they live now ?
Not in the grave, they say,
Then where now ?

Tell me, tell me,
Is it where I may go ?
Ask not, cries the holm-oak,
Weep, says snow.

STEVIE SMITH

I sit up and bellow : Death,
then it is
time for the
party !—we
draw decanters out of the coffin, tear in our
teeth the candy lilies. Ah, the
trumpets' Reveille, the
rollicking floor ! Open the windows,
Jock ! My
beauties, my
noble horses—yoked in
pairs, white horses, drawing my great
hearse, galloping and
frolicking over the cropped turf.

D. M. BLACK

The Old Women

Go sad or sweet or riotous with beer
Past the old women gossiping by the hour,
They'll fix on you from every close and pier
An acid look to make your veins run sour.

'No help,' they say, 'his grandfather that's dead
Was troubled with the same dry-throated curse,
And many a night he made the ditch his bed.
This blood comes welling from the same cracked
source.'

On every kind of merriment they frown.
But I have known a gray-eyed sober boy
Sail to the lobsters in a storm, and drown.
Over his body dripping on the stones
Those same old hags would weave into their moans
An undersong of terrible holy joy.

GEORGE MACKAY BROWN

Mrs Root

Busybody, nosey-parker
lacking the vast discretion of most
was this woman. The self-cast
chief mourner at funerals, worker
at weddings, she could sniff out death
in a doctor's optimism, joggle
a maiden's mind (button-holed on the front path)
till virginity bit like filed teeth.

Prepared, without discrimination,
friend and enemy for the grave.
Washed, talcumed them all. A woman
who wore such ceremonies like a glove,
could console a grief-struck household
that hardly knew her name, and then
collect money for a wreath fit to wield
at a Queen's passing. Death-skilled

but no less wedding-wise,
her hand stitched the perfecting dart
in bridal satin ; she brought report
of cars arriving, clear skies
towards the church. They were her tears
(pew-stifled) from which the happiest
laughter billowed confetti outside the church doors.
Of best wishes, loudest were hers.

And nobody thanked her ; Why doesn't
she mind her own business ?, they said
who'd leant upon her. Crude and peasant-like
her interest in brides, and the dead.
I thought so too, yet still was loath
to add my voice, sensing that
my secret poems were like her actions : both
pried into love and savoured death.

TONY CONNOR

Poor Women in a City Church

The small wax candles melt to light,
Flicker in marble, reflect bright
Asterisks on brass candlesticks :
At the Virgin's altar on the right
Blue flames are jerking on wicks.

Old dough-faced women with black shawls
Drawn down tight kneel in the stalls.
Cold yellow candle-tongues, blue flame
Mince and caper as whispered calls
Take wing up to the Holy Name.

Thus each day in the sacred place
They kneel. Golden shrines, altar lace,
Marble columns and cool shadows
Still them. In the gloom you cannot trace
A wrinkle on their beeswax brows.

SEAMUS HEANEY

An Arundel Tomb

Side by side, their faces blurred,
The earl and countess lie in stone,
Their proper habits vaguely shown
As jointed armour, stiffened pleat,
And that faint hint of the absurd—
The little dogs under their feet.

Such plainness of the pre-baroque
Hardly involves the eye, until
It meets his left-hand gauntlet, still
Clasped empty in the other ; and
One sees, with a sharp tender shock,
His hand withdrawn, holding her hand.

They would not think to lie so long.
Such faithfulness in effigy
Was just a detail friends would see :
A sculptor's sweet commissioned grace
Thrown off in helping to prolong
The Latin names around the base.

They would not guess how early in
Their supine stationary voyage
The air would change to soundless damage,
Turn the old tenantry away ;
How soon succeeding eyes begin
To look, not read. Rigidly they

Persisted, linked, through lengths and breadths
Of time. Snow fell, undated. Light
Each summer thronged the glass. A bright
Litter of birdcalls strewed the same
Bone-riddled ground. And up the paths
The endless altered people came,

Washing at their identity.
Now, helpless in the hollow of
An unarmorial age, a trough
Of smoke in slow suspended skeins
Above their scrap of history,
Only an attitude remains :

Time has transfigured them into
Untruth. The stone fidelity
They hardly meant has come to be
Their final blazon, and to prove
Our almost-instinct almost true:
What will survive of us is love.

PHILIP LARKIN

Here

I am a man now.
Pass your hand over my brow :
You can feel the place where the brains grow.

I am like a tree :
From my top boughs I can see
The footprints that led up to me.

There is blood in my veins
That has run clear of the stain
Contracted in so many loins.

Why, then, are my hands red
With the blood of so many dead ?
Is this where I was misled ?

Why are my hands this way
That they will not do as I say ?
Does no God hear when I pray ?

I have nowhere to go.
The swift satellites show
The clock of my whole being is slow.

It is too late to start
For destinations not of the heart.
I must stay here with my hurt.

R. S. THOMAS

A Small Consolation

The imperceptible units of decay
　　Litter my rooms: echoes of words,
Holes of silences, bitterness
　　Malevolent as weed in corners.

How many miles of pared
　　Fingernails, of shed hair, and skin
Whose flakes, collected,
　　Might bury me in my own dross?

Sometimes waking at night
　　In darkness that is years of my closed eyes
I know that I lie
　　Already stifled by layers of past self;

And I would cry out
　　But griefs long since exhaled
Wash back from the walls, and I choke
　　In a tide of stagnant, long-shed tears.

I am ordinary, and have been fearful of dying;
　　But now I perceive
With a wry acceptance that so much of me has
departed
　　There is little left to suffer.

So I turn to sleep
　　Under the adulterous wave of yawns and sighs
Already spent, consoled that thus I may exit
　　Noiselessly, like a shadow, unnoticed through a
small door.

JOHN SMITH

Oblivion

It was a human face in my oblivion
A human being and a human voice
That cried to me, Come back, come back, come
back.
But I would not, I said I would not come back.

It was so sweet in my oblivion
There was a sweet mist wrapped me round about
And I trod in a sweet and milky sea, knee deep,
That was so pretty and so beautiful, growing deeper.

But still the voice cried out, Come back, come back,
Come back to me from sweet oblivion!
It was a human and related voice
That cried to me in pain. So I turned back.

I cannot help but like oblivion better
Than being a human heart and a human creature,
But I can wait for her, her gentle mist
And those sweet seas that deepen are my destiny
And must come even if not soon.

STEVIE SMITH

Do Not Go Gentle Into That Good Night

Do not go gentle into that good night,
Old age should burn and rave at close of day;
Rage, rage against the dying of the light.

Though wise men at their end know dark is right,
Because their words have forked no lightning they
Do not go gentle into that good night.

Good men, the last wave by, crying how bright
Their frail deeds might have danced in a green bay,
Rage, rage against the dying of the light.

Wild men who caught and sang the sun in flight
And learn, too late, they grieved it on its way,
Do not go gentle into that good night.

Grave men, near death, who see with blinding sight
Blind eyes could blaze like meteors and be gay,
Rage, rage against the dying of the light.

And you, my father, there on the sad height,
Curse, bless, me now with your fierce tears, I pray.
Do not go gentle into that good night.
Rage, rage against the dying of the light.

DYLAN THOMAS

In The Night

Out of my window late at night I gape
And see the stars but do not watch them really,
And hear the trains but do not listen clearly ;
Inside my mind I turn about to keep
Myself awake, yet am not there entirely.
Something of me is out in the dark landscape.

How much am I then what I think, how much what
I feel ?
How much the eye that seems to keep stars straight ?
Do I control what I can contemplate
Or is it my vision that's amenable ?
I turn in my mind, my mind is a room whose wall
I can see the top of but never completely scale.

All that I love is, like the night, outside,
Good to be gazed at, looking as if it could
With a simple gesture be brought inside my head
Or in my heart. But my thoughts about it divide
Me from my object. Now deep in my bed
I turn and the world turns on the other side.

ELIZABETH JENNINGS

The Secret Sharer

Over the ankles in snow and numb past pain
I stared up at my window three stories high :
From a white street unconcerned as a dead eye,
I patiently called my name again and again.

The curtains were lit, through glass were lit by doubt
And there was I, within the room alone.
In the empty wind I stood and shouted on :
But O, what if the strange head should peer out ?

Suspended taut between two equal fears
I was like to be torn apart by their strong pull :
What, I asked, if I never hear my call ?
And what if it reaches my insensitive ears ?

Fixed in my socket of thought I saw them move
Aside, I saw that some uncertain hand
Had touched the curtains. Mine, I wondered ? And,
At this instant, the wind turned in its groove.

The wind turns in its groove and I am here
Lying in bed, the snow and street outside ;
Fire-glow still reassuring ; dark defied.
The wind turns in its groove : I am still there.

THOM GUNN

Counting the Beats

You, love, and I,
(He whispers) you and I,
And if no more than only you and I
What care you or I?

Counting the beats,
Counting the slow heart beats,
The bleeding to death of time in slow heart beats,
Wakeful they lie.

Cloudless day,
Night, and a cloudless day,
Yet the huge storm will burst upon their heads one day
From a bitter sky.

Where shall we be,
(She whispers) where shall we be,
When death strikes home, O where then shall we be
Who were you and I?

Not there but here,
(He whispers) only here,
As we are, here, together, now and here,
Always you and I.

Counting the beats,
Counting the slow heart beats,
The bleeding to death of time in slow heart beats,
Wakeful they lie.

ROBERT GRAVES

First, Goodbye

First, you will say goodbye. You will turn
   And for what you think is the last time gaze from the window
   To the bright and battering street headlong below.
Behind your eyes, your smile, the tears will burn.

You will not let them fall. You will stand
   As if you were a child or a cripple unable to walk.
   You will try though the words are like glass,
   you will try to talk,
But you will manage only a pathetic gesture of the hand.

All this is ordinary. You will be aware
   Of my presence behind you the world of our words away.
   And you will know, you will know there is
   nothing that I can say;
And then you will hear with your heart the dumbness of my despair

Articulate in the silence; it will cry
   Out in such a remonstrance of love that you will know
   No window or door or street may let you go,
Or your lips or my lips utter a last goodbye.

JOHN SMITH

Song For Isolde

The parting has come as we knew it would:
The same silence that held our bodies tense
Reading sonnets in our eyes now holds us
Apart in an elegy of lost dreams.

I felt like Orpheus at that moment. A
Furtive glance might have missed your eyes and so
Blurred their love in my memory. Now my
Empty arms cling to that final image . . .

You with your hand at your lips, eyes grey with
Longing. The earth stops turning and life holds
Its breath taut waiting for Fate's leaden seal.
And then it comes, as nothing happens . . . For

I could not turn to watch you go, or stay
When you had gone. The wind shivered and the hills
Withdrew, leaving an empty landscape for me
To search, like an old man poking hot ashes.

ERIC WILLIAMS

Song

O lady, when the tipped cup of the moon blessed
you
You became soft fire with a cloud's grace;
The difficult stars swam for eyes in your face;
You stood, and your shadow was my place:
You turned, your shadow turned to ice
    O my lady.

O lady, when the sea caressed you
You were a marble of foam, but dumb.
When will the stone open its tomb?
When will the waves give over their foam?
You will not die, nor come home,
    O my lady.

O lady, when the wind kissed you
You made him music for you were a shaped shell.
I follow the waters and the wind still
Since my heart heard it and all to pieces fell
Which your lovers stole, meaning ill,
    O my lady.

O lady, consider when I shall have lost you
The moon's full hands, scattering waste,
The sea's hands, dark from the world's breast,
The world's decay where the wind's hands have
passed,
And my head, worn out with love, at rest
In my hands, and my hands full of dust,
    O my lady.

TED HUGHES

Your Cry

Your mouth, a thread of dying grass
Sealed to its lower lip,
At last is opening. We are alone,
You used to say,
And in each other's care.

Your cry
Has interrupted nothing and our hands,
Limp in each other's hair,
Have lost their touch.

IAN HAMILTON

The Feel of Hands

The hands explore tentatively,
two small live entities whose shapes
I have to guess at. They touch me
all, with the light of fingertips

testing each surface of each thing
found, timid as kittens with it.
I connect them with amusing
hands I have shaken by daylight.

There is a sudden transition :
they plunge together in a full
formed single fury ; they are grown
to cats, hunting without scruple ;

They are expert but desperate.
I am in the dark. I wonder
when they grew up. It strikes me that
I do not know whose hands they are.

One Flesh

Lying apart now, each in a separate bed,
He with a book, keeping the light on late,
She like a girl dreaming of childhood,
All men elsewhere—it is as if they wait
Some new event : the book he holds unread,
Her eyes fixed on the shadows overhead.

Tossed up like flotsam from a former passion,
How cool they lie. They hardly ever touch,
Or if they do it is like a confession
Of having little feeling—or too much.
Chastity faces them, a destination
For which their whole lives were a preparation.

Strangely apart, yet strangely close together,
Silence between them like a thread to hold
And not wind in. And time itself's a feather
Touching them gently. Do they know they're old,
These two who are my father and my mother
Whose fire from which I came, has now grown
cold ?

ELIZABETH JENNINGS

THOM GUNN

On a Summer Night

'The moon, my love, deceives, O many, many,'
    He says. She says :
    'Then let us not look up ;'
kissing his shadowed face, turning her money.

'I was long since lost in the deserts of women,'
    He says. She says :
    'Lie down in this cool place,'
and strokes his lips, her hand as slow as famine.

'Has the wind dropped ? Is that the rain falling ?'
    He says. She says :
    'Tighten your arms around me ;
it is only the stars' flight, the earth rolling.'

'And will this night, then, not go on for ever ?'
    He says. She says :
    'Quiet my love, be quiet ;
sleep is full of bad dreams but will soon be over.'

STEVIE SMITH

The Sea-Widow

How fares it with you, Mrs Cooper my bride ?
Long are the years since you lay by my side.
Do you wish I was back ? Do you speak of me
dearest ?
I wish you were back for me to hold nearest.
Who then lies nearer, Mrs Cooper my bride ?
A black man comes in with the evening tide.
What is his name ? Tell me ! How does he dare ?
He comes uninvited. His name is Despair.

TONY CONNOR

Old Couple

We know no other daylight now,
except such little as may lie
along dark folds of drapery

mornings, evenings, the sun low
enough to find a shafted way
to us through a bolted window.

Little enough there is left
for us to need between the sun
of morning after we have lain

long, and sun of evening, soft
on the folds, before once again
we lie out all the night bereft

of sleep, thought, sensation. A bed
is all we have to own, to know
the limits of our limbs in ; grow

a little feebler in. No need
remains for us, save only to
sense when one of us is dead

when the one of us will be dead.

TED WALKER

A Dream of Hanging

He rang me up
In a dream,
My brother did.
He had been hanged
That morning,
Innocent,
And I had slept
Through the striking
Of the clock
While it had taken place,
Eight,
Just about time enough
For it to happen.
He spoke to me
On the telephone
That afternoon
To reassure me,
My dear brother
Who had killed nobody,
And I asked him,
Long distance,
What it had felt like
To be hanged.
'Oh, don't worry, lovey,' he said,
'When your time comes.
It tickled rather.'

PATRICIA BEER

At the Florist's

A man enters a florist's
and chooses some flowers
the florist wraps up the flowers
the man puts his hand in his pocket
to find the money
the money to pay for the flowers
but at the same time he puts
all of a sudden
his hand on his heart
and he falls

At the same time that he falls
the money rolls on the floor
and then the flowers fall
at the same time as the man
at the same time as the money
and the florist stands there
with the money rolling
with the flowers spoiling
with the man dying
obviously all this is very sad
and she's got to do something
the florist
but she doesn't know quite where to start
she doesn't know
at which end to begin

There's so many things to do
with this man dying
with these flowers spoiling
and this money
this money that rolls
that doesn't stop rolling.

JACQUES PRÉVERT, *translated by*
LAWRENCE FERLINGHETTI

The Stranger

'Look quickly !' said the stranger
I turned around in time to see
a wall fall onto the child
playing beside a derelict house
In the silence of the rising dust
I saw the child's arm thrust
out stiff between the bricks
like a tulip
   a white tulip

         a clenched tulip

I turned angrily to the stranger
'Why did you have to tell me ?'
'Well I thought you'd want to see' he said
the tulip screamed
    now limp

        now red

ROGER MCGOUGH

The Suspect

Asked me for a match suddenly / with his hand up
I thought he was after my wallet
gave him a shove / he fell down
dead on the pavement at my feet
he was forty-two, a respectable man they said

anyone can have a bad heart I told the police
but they've held me five hours and don't
tell me the innocent don't feel
guilty in the glaring chair

I didn't kill you / I didn't know you
I did push you / I did fear you
accusing me from the mortuary drawer
like a damned white ghost I don't believe in
—then why were you afraid / are you used to attacks
by men who want a match / what sort
of life you lead / you were bloody quick
with your hands when you pushed him
what did you think he was and do you think
we don't know what you are / take it
all down / the sweat of the innocent by god we'll see
and not by the hundred-watt bulb of the anglepoise
either
give him a clip on the ear jack / you
bastard in your shroud if I feared you then
I hate you now you
no I don't you poor dead man I put you there
I don't I don't
but just

if you could get up / to speak for me
I am on trial / do you understand
I am not guilty / whatever the light says
whatever the sweat says
/ they've noticed my old scar
to be killed by a dead man is no fight
they're starting again
so / your story is he asked you for a light
—yes suddenly / and put his hand up / I thought
he was after my wallet, gave him
a shove, he fell as I told you
dead, it was his heart,
at my feet, as I said

EDWIN MORGAN

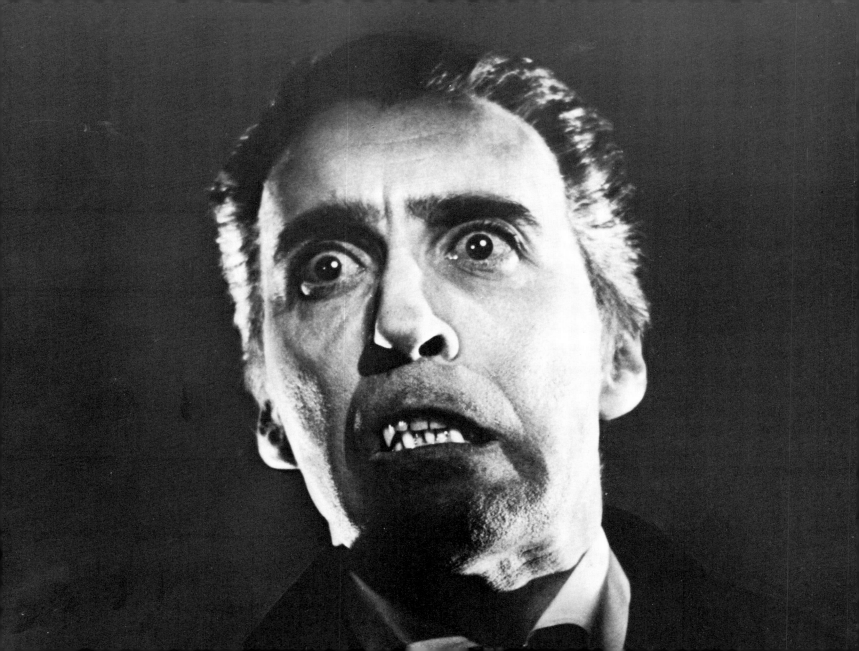

The Beast

Something that was not there before
has come through the mirror
into my room.

It is not such a simple creature
as at first I thought—
from somewhere it has brought a mischief

that troubles both silence and objects
and now left alone here
I weave intricate reasons for its arrival.

They disintegrate. Today in January, with
the light frozen on my window, I hear outside
a million panicking birds, and know even out there

comfort is done with ; it has shattered
even the stars, this creature
at last come home to me.

BRIAN PATTEN

Report on August

How do I sleep ? Well, but
the dreams are bad :

filled with accusations
small but just.

These slack summer dawns
that fail of sunrise

There's a relief at falling
awake and into comfort,

becoming once again
four people, watching

from pillow level
my boys' khaki heads bustle about :

over breakfast I see,
staring at the garden,

how the times have fed ;
under heavy leaves and low sky

in profile the bold woodpigeon
walks the lawn

Beats of a shadowy fanblade
tick through from behind,

time going ; ignored,
nobody measuring time, so much

constant, the weather unchanging,
the work I do filling days

so that they seem one day,
a firm framework, made

of the window where I sit
(or lie, slumped, feet on the desk,

waved to by passers-by
like a paraplegic)

a window-shaped guise of myself
that holds what few events come round

like slides, and in what seems
capricious sequence.

ROY FISHER

Song

What day is it
It's everyday
My friend
It's all of life
My love
We love each other and we live
We live and love each other
And do not know what this life is
And do not know what this day is
And do not know what this love is.

JACQUES PRÉVERT *translated by*
LAWRENCE FERLINGHETTI

My Face Is My Own, I Thought

morning   he had gone
down to the village   a figure
she still recognized from his walk

nothing
        he had explained
is won by arguing   things are changed
only by power
                and cunning   she still sat
meaning to ask what
did you say   ?   echo in her ears

he might just have finished speaking   so
waiting and
            taking the scissors
began to trim off the baby's fingers

TOM RAWORTH

Her Husband

Comes home dull with coal-dust deliberately
To grime the sink and foul towels and let her
Learn with scrubbing brush and scrubbing board
The stubborn character of money.

And let her learn through what kind of dust
He has earned his thirst and the right to quench it
And what sweat he has exchanged for his money
And the blood-weight of money. He'll humble her

With new light on her obligations.
The fried, woody chips, kept warm two hours in
the oven,
Are only part of her answer.
Hearing the rest he slams them to the fire back

And is away round the house-end singing
'Come back to Sorrento' in a voice
Of resounding corrugated iron.
Her back has bunched into a hump as an insult.

For they will have their rights.
Their jurors are to be assembled
From the little crumbs of soot. Their brief
Goes straight up to heaven and nothing more is
heard of it.

TED HUGHES

Breakfast

He put the coffee
In the cup
He put the milk
In the cup of coffee
He put the sugar
In the *café au lait*
With the coffee spoon
He stirred
He drank the *café au lait*
And he set down the cup
Without a word to me
He lit
A cigarette
He made smoke-rings
With the smoke
He put the ashes
In the ash-tray
Without a word to me
Without a look at me
He got up
He put
His hat upon his head
He put his raincoat on
Because it was raining
And he left
In the rain
Without a word
Without a look at me
And I I took
My head in my hand
And I cried.

JACQUES PRÉVERT,

translated by

LAWRENCE FERLINGHETTI

Ghosts

Those houses haunt in which we leave
Something undone. It is not those
Great words or silences of love

That spread their echoes through a place
And fill the locked-up unbreathed gloom.
Ghosts do not haunt with any face

That we have known ; they only come
With arrogance to thrust at us
Our own omissions in a room.

The words we would not speak they use,
The deeds we dared not act they flaunt,
Our nervous silences they bruise ;

It is our helplessness they choose
And our refusals that they haunt.

ELIZABETH JENNINGS

Road Song

This evening at least I do not care
where the journey will be ending ;
only a landscape softened now
by song and slow rainfall fills me.

The rest of things, her body crushed
against the whitest pillows, regrets
and the more concrete failures
are exiled and done with.

There is nowhere specially to get to.
The towns are identical, each one passed

takes deeper into evening
what sorrows I've brought with me.

In my head some voice is singing
a song that once linked us ;
it has ceased to be of importance ;
another song might replace it.

Now only my gawky shadow occupies
these roads going nowhere,
that by small towns are linked
and that by the darkness are cancelled.

BRIAN PATTEN

Lonely Man

An open world
    within its mountain rim :
trees on the plain lifting
    their heads, fine strokes
    of grass stretching themselves to breathe
the last of the light.
                Where a man
riding horseback raises dust
    under the eucalyptus trees, a long way off,
    the dust
is gray-gold, a cloud
    of pollen. A field
    of cosmea turns
    all its many faces
of wide-open flowers west, to the light.

It is your loneliness
your energy
    baffled in the stillness
    gives an edge to the shadows—
the great sweep of mountain shadow,
shadows of ants and leaves,
    the stones of the road each with its shadow
and you with your long shadow
closing your book and standing up
to stretch, your long shadow-arms
    stretching back of you, baffled.

DENISE LEVERTOV

Mr Bleaney

'This was Mr Bleaney's room. He stayed
The whole time he was at the Bodies, till
They moved him.' Flowered curtains, thin and frayed,
Fall to within five inches of the sill,

Whose window shows a strip of building land,
Tussocky, littered. 'Mr Bleaney took
My bit of garden properly in hand.'
Bed, upright chair, sixty-watt bulb, no hook

Behind the door, no room for books or bags—
'I'll take it.' So it happens that I lie
Where Mr Bleaney lay, and stub my fags
On the same saucer-souvenir, and try

Stuffing my ears with cotton-wool, to drown
The jabbering set he egged her on to buy.
I know his habits—what time he came down,
His preference for sauce to gravy, why

He kept on plugging at the four aways—
Likewise their yearly frame : the Frinton folk
Who put him up for summer holidays,
And Christmas at his sister's house in Stoke.

But if he stood and watched the frigid wind
Tousling the clouds, lay on the fusty bed
Telling himself that this was home, and grinned,
And shivered, without shaking off the dread

That how we live measures our own nature,
And at his age having no more to show
Than one hired box should make him pretty sure
He warranted no better, I don't know.

PHILIP LARKIN

An Irish Monk, on Lindisfarne, about 650 A.D.

A hesitation of the tide
betrays this island, daily.

On Iona, at dusk
(ago, how long ago ?)
often (did it happen ?)
I saw the Lord walking
in the surf amidst the gulls,
calling, 'Come. Have joy in Me.'

Yes, with these eyes.
Now, on strange rocks
(faintly through the wall)
echoing, the same sea roars.

Detail is my toil.
In chapel, verse by verse—
in the kitchen, loaf by loaf—
with my pen, word by word—

by imitation,
illumination.

The patience of the bricklayer
is assumed in the dream of the architect.

On the road coming, five days travel, a Pict woman (big mouth and small bones) gave me shelter, and laughed (part scorn, part pity) at my journey. 'What do you hope for, even if you get there, that you couldn't have had twice over in Ireland?'

Then I told her of the darkness amongst the barbarians and of the great light in the monasteries at home, and she replied, 'Will they thank you for that, you so young and naive, and why should you go, you out of so many?'

I said that I heard a voice calling, and she said, 'So men dream, are unsatisfied, wear their legs out with walking, and you scarcely a boy out of school.'

So she laughed, and I leaned my head on my hands, feeling the thickness of dust in each palm.

Then she told me there was not another of her face left in that valley, not one, nothing left.' And all in three generations. Once even Rome feared us. Now my children are mongrels. And my husband has left me. No matter. Or great matter. I am still a Pict.'

Then she fed me, put herbs on my feet, wished me well, and I blessed her but she said, 'Save that for yourself, you will need it, when your heart turns rancid, and your joints begin to stiffen on the foreign roads. Remember me, when you come, returning.'

So she mocked; and sometimes, even now, ten years later, I hear it as I waken (receding in a dream), that laughter, broad, without malice.

Returning,
in the mind, still there,
home :
—devout green hills
—intimate peat smoke
—a cow-bell beseeching
—warm fleece in my bed
—fresh water, fresh, a brook

Here :
—rain clouds like beggars' rags
—stench of burned weed
—fret of the chain-mail sea
—hard knees on cold stone
—dry saliva, salt fish

The gulls cry :
—believe
—achieve

The bells reply :
—some
—some

At the lowest ebb
you can leave dryshod
this fitful island

GAEL TURNBULL

The Last of the Peasantry

What does he know ? moving through the fields
And the wood's echoing cloisters
With a beast's gait, hunger in his eyes
Only for what the flat earth supplies ;
His wisdom dwindled to a small gift
For handling stock, planting a few seeds
To ripen slowly in the warm breath
Of an old God to whom he never prays.

Moving through the fields, or still at home,
Dwarfed by his shadow on the bright wall,
His face is lit always from without,
The sun by day, the red fire at night ;
Within is dark and bare, the grey ash
Is cold now, blow on it as you will.

R. S. THOMAS

Moving Through the Silent Crowd

Moving through the silent crowd
Who stand behind dull cigarettes
These men who idle in the road,
I have the sense of falling light.

They lounge at corners of the street
And greet friends with a shrug of shoulder
And turn their empty pockets out,
The cynical gestures of the poor.

Now they've no work, like better men
Who sit at desks and take much pay
They sleep long nights and rise at ten
To watch the hours that drain away.

I'm jealous of the weeping hours
They stare through with such hungry eyes.
I'm haunted by these images,
I'm haunted by their emptiness.

STEPHEN SPENDER

Toyland

Today the sunlight is the paint on lead soldiers
Only they are people scattering out of the cool church

And as they go across the gravel and among the spring streets
They spread formality : they know, we know, what they have been doing,

The old couples, the widowed, the staunch smilers,
The deprived and the few nubile young lily-ladies,

And we know what they will do when they have opened the doors of their houses and walked in :
Mostly they will make water, and wash their calm hands and eat.

The organ's flourishes finish ; the verger closes the doors ;
The choirboys run home, and the rector goes off in his motor.

Here a policeman stalks, the sun glinting on his helmet-crest ;
Then a man pushes a perambulator home ; and somebody posts a letter.

If I sit here long enough, loving it all, I shall see the District Nurse pedal past,
The children going to Sunday School and the strollers strolling ;

The lights darting on in different rooms as night comes in ;
And I shall see washing hung out, and the postman delivering letters.

I might by exception see an ambulance or the fire brigade
Or even, if the chance came round, street musicians (singing and playing).

For the people I've seen, this seems the operation of life :
I need the paint of stillness and sunshine to see it that way.

The secret laugh of the world picks them up and shakes them like peas boiling ;
They behave as if nothing happened ; maybe they no longer notice.

I notice. I laugh with the laugh, cultivate it, make much of it,
But I still don't know what the joke is, to tell them.

ROY FISHER

Thinks

you think
it can't last
it should all be over by midnight
or tomorrow lunchtime at the outside

but it goes on
and nobody stoops
to handle the brake

it goes on
and very soon you get to understand
that
perhaps it will last after all
pretty soon you get to saying to yourself

I must do something
about this

so you settle down with a good book
under the arc lamps of reality
you dissect the words
and keep them in vinegar
you take a little love
and you bruise it in your palm
you take a little hope
and boil it in your fear
you laugh a little
cry a little
start to blow your nose
and you think

perhaps a storm would turn off the sun
perhaps we'll all learn to work out the facts

so you put out the flags
as you turn out the lights
and much later

about a lifetime
later

one dark night
in the cold of your bed
you sit up with a start
with a voice in your head

and you say to yourself

I must do something
about this

MILES GIBSON

South London Prose Poem

Sunset over a waste of allotments tended by gnomes: rows of squat houses with lazily smoking chimneys. Small gnomish houses surrounded by a waste of decaying allotments tended by dwarfish men smoking pipes.

Rows of painted brick houses and untidy back gardens, cabbage plots and patches of weedstrewn earth narrowly bisected by wandering muddy paths. A slow dreamy sunset curling away over the dark rooves of dwarfish little houses inhabited by gnomes tending their decaying allotments.

Cabbage patches and small fields of earth and stones divided by scrubby hedgerows and pipesmoking gnomes carefully tending their unkempt gardens. The magnificent red sunset curling diaphanously into the heavens over a blue haze rising from the smoking bonfires and smoking chimneys of a smallish gnomish people meticulously tending to their weedstrewn allotments. Red clouds unfolding over fields of bare earth and row upon row of forlorn cabbage plants tenderly weeded by pipesmoking thoughtful gnomes. Need I say more. Need I say more? Have I missed anything?

O yes and I sit in my smallish gnomish room with Westerly view sketching out over the rooftops the curling diaphanous clouds of the sunset folding on to the dark rooves of a beetle-browed smallish gnomish people carefully cultivating their smallholdings of lonely cabbage plants and bare areas of weedy, unkempt earth.

CHRIS TORRANCE

No Place

I was brought down
in suburbs;
nurtured on asphalt,
stared up at the sky
through saw-tooth Tudor.
Gates with rising suns,
gardens with plaster dwarfs
bounded my—what?
childhood? I peeped
through featherboard fences
at lawns lost in trees,
tennis courts and space

I knew I could fill.
Now I can go, be
anyone anywhere, slough
off the concrete shell
of rebellion. Leave my—what?
Self? Like the tennis ball
in somebody's dahlias,
tip-toeing quietly away,
afraid of the sudden shout,
and half-hoping it comes.

JOHN DANIEL

Well It Has Been a Pleasure England

Well it has been a great old
party the first one said starting
on down the stairs a
great gettogether the second
one joining in all the others
pushing out into the stair-
case following them
on down talking and
singing and laughing like
mad supporting each
other stopping to pick up
this and that on the way
down the stairs a great
great long party winding on
down a merry old dragon of
Chinamen retelling itself
what jokes writing them
down on the walls for those
who came after stumbling
and hopping on down so pleased
No one noticed they must've
been going on down for at
least a month and well
            below
                street-
                    level

ANSELM HOLLO

Good Friday

Three o'clock. The bus lurches
round into the sun. 'D's this go—'
he flops beside me—'right along Bath Street?
—Oh tha's, tha's all right, see I've
got to get some Easter eggs for the kiddies.
I've had a wee drink, ye understand—
ye'll maybe think it's a—funny day
to be celebrating—well, no, but ye see
I wasny working, and I like to celebrate
when I'm no working—I don't say it's right
I'm no saying it's right, ye understand—ye
understand?
But anyway tha's the way I look at it—
I'm no boring you, eh?—ye see today,
take today, I don't know what today's in aid of,
whether Christ was—crucified or was he—
rose fae the dead like, see what I mean?
You're an educatit man, you can tell me—
—Aye, well. There ye are. It's been seen
time and again, the working man
has nae education, he jist canny—jist
hasny got it, know what I mean,
he's jist bliddy ignorant—Christ aye,
bliddy ignorant. Well—'The bus brakes violently,
he lunges for the stair, swings down—off,
into the sun for his Easter eggs,
on very
            nearly
                steady
                  legs.

EDWIN MORGAN

Postcard

Snow fell on London Zoo. The Polar bears
Turned grey in half an hour. Quickly they stopped
Looking at the North, for it came flying past.
They saw the cold for the first time in years,
Choosing and nosing one piece as it dropped,
One flake to them smelling of all the rest.

There are advantages in any prison.
Bears have more food here, more security,
Freedom to breed though not much wish to do so.
But now the air is visible and the season
Can be touched, now that they feel and see
Their white stone ledge upholstered into snow,

They sicken for the perils of their home.
We are all lucky perhaps to live away
From danger, to receive only a few
Random cold flakes of fear out of the storm
Massing somewhere else. Yet on a day
Like this, the only safety seems to be

In the great blizzard playing at the pole,
Where danger could become our native land,
The central place, inside this fringe of fear.
And every touch of snow seems to recall
Some light and menacing postcard from a friend,
'Having a lovely time. Wish you were here.'

PATRICIA BEER

Rock n' Roll Poem

PETER FINCH

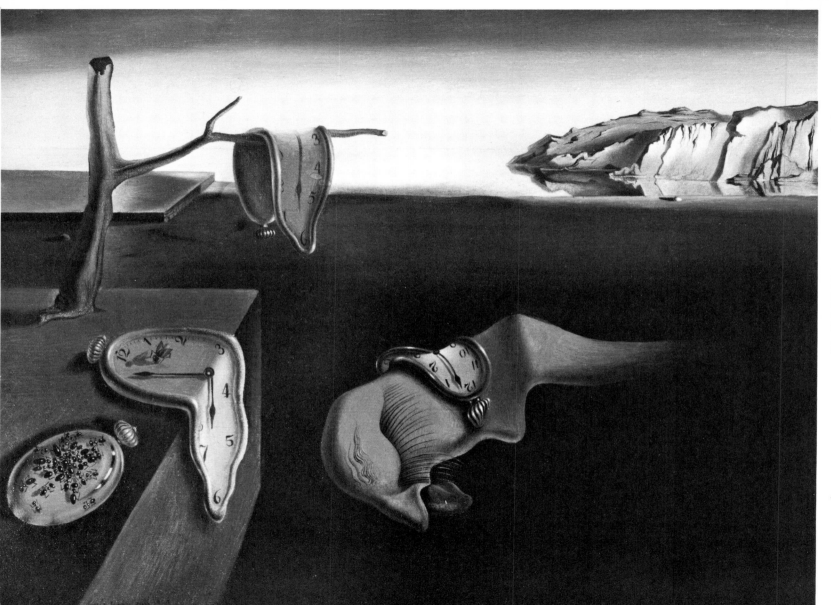

The Slow Starter

A watched clock never moves, they said :
Leave it alone and you'll grow up.
Nor will the sulking holiday train
Start sooner if you stamp your feet.
  He left the clock to go its way ;
  The whistle blew, the train went gay.

Do not press me so, she said ;
Leave me alone and I will write
But not just yet, I am sure you know
The problem. Do not count the days.
  He left the calendar alone ;
  The postman knocked, no letter came.

O never force the pace, they said ;
Leave it alone, you have lots of time,
Your kind of work is none the worse
For slow maturing. Do not rush.
  He took their tip, he took his time,
  And found his time and talent gone.

Oh you have had your chance, I said ;
Left it alone and it was one.
Who said a watched clock never moves ?
Look at it now. Your chance was I.
  He turned and saw the accusing clock
  Race like a torrent round a rock.

LOUIS MACNEICE

Poem

A year
burning away time.

Where are the words ?

The room
was full of people,
but they didn't speak.

A year
without love or hate—

no natural
cleansing or disfigurement—

lying awake,
watching the car lights play
and the branched wind wash the walls, until life

is another form of time
without substance, breathing.

America.
One more rash of lights
in an interminable orbit. Round

and round,
the earth, the moon—

praying for that innocence now
which must keep talking,

or stops forever.

DAVID WEVILL

Will It Be So Again?

Will it be so again
That the brave, the gifted are lost from view,
And empty, scheming men
Are left in peace their lunatic age to renew?
Will it be so again?

Must it be always so
That the best are chosen to fall and sleep
Like seeds, and we too slow
In claiming the earth they quicken, and the old
usurpers reap
What they could not sow?

Will it be so again—
The jungle code and the hypocrite gesture?
A poppy wreath for the slain
And a cut-throat world for the living? that stale
imposture
Played on us once again?

Will it be as before—
Peace, with no heart or mind to ensure it,
Guttering down to war
Like a libertine to his grave? We should not be
surprised: we knew it
Happen before.

Shall it be so again?
Call not upon the glorious dead
To be your witnesses then.
The living alone can nail to their promise the ones
who said
It shall not be so again.

C. DAY LEWIS

Your Attention Please

The Polar DEW has just warned that
A nuclear rocket strike of
At least one thousand megatons
Has been launched by the enemy
Directly at our major cities.
This announcement will take
Two and a quarter minutes to make,
You therefore have a further
Eight and a quarter minutes
To comply with the shelter
Requirements published in the Civil
Defence Code—section Atomic Attack.
A specially shortened Mass
Will be broadcast at the end
Of this announcement—
Protestant and Jewish services
Will begin simultaneously—
Select your wavelength immediately
According to instructions
In the Defence Code. Do not
Take well-loved pets (including birds)
Into your shelter—they will consume
Fresh air. Leave the old and bed-
ridden, you can do nothing for them.
Remember to press the sealing
Switch when everyone is in
The shelter. Set the radiation
Aerial, turn on the geiger barometer.
Turn off your Television now.
Turn off your radio immediately
The Services end. At the same time
Secure explosion plugs in the ears

Of each member of your family. Take
Down your plasma flasks. Give your children
The pills marked one and two
In the C.D. green container, then put
Them to bed. Do not break
The inside airlock seals until
The radiation All Clear shows
(Watch for the cuckoo in your
perspex panel), or your District
Touring Doctor rings your bell.
If before this, your air becomes
Exhausted or if any of your family
Is critically injured, administer
The capsules marked 'Valley Forge'
(Red pocket in No. 1 Survival Kit)
For painless death. (Catholics
Will have been instructed by their priests
What to do in this eventuality.)
This announcement is ending. Our President
Has already given orders for
Massive retaliation—it will be
Decisive. Some of us may die.
Remember, statistically
It is not likely to be you.
All flags are flying fully dressed
On Government buildings—the sun is shining.
Death is the least we have to fear.
We are all in the hands of God.
Whatever happens happens by His Will.
Now go quickly to your shelters.

PETER PORTER

Five Ways to Kill a Man

There are many cumbersome ways to kill a man.
You can make him carry a plank of wood
to the top of a hill and nail him to it. To do this
properly you require a crowd of people
wearing sandals, a cock that crows, a cloak
to dissect, a sponge, some vinegar and one
man to hammer the nails home.

Or you can take a length of steel,
shaped and chased in a traditional way,
and attempt to pierce the metal cage he wears.
But for this you need white horses,
English trees, men with bows and arrows,
at least two flags, a prince, and a
castle to hold your banquet in.

Dispensing with nobility, you may, if the wind
allows, blow gas at him. But then you need
a mile of mud sliced through with ditches,
not to mention black boots, bomb craters,
more mud, a plague of rats, a dozen songs
and some round hats made of steel.

In an age of aeroplanes, you may fly
miles above your victim and dispose of him by
pressing one small switch. All you then
require is an ocean to separate you, two
systems of government, a nations's scientists,
several factories, a psychopath and
land that no-one needs for several years.

These are, as I began, cumbersome ways
to kill a man. Simpler, direct, and much more neat
is to see that he is living somewhere in the middle
of the twentieth century, and leave him there.

EDWIN BROCK

The Silent Piano

We have lived like civilized people.
O ruins, traditions !

And we have seen the barbarians,
breakers of sculpture and glass.

And now we talk of 'the inner life',
and I ask myself, where is it ?

Not here, in these streets and houses,
so I think it must be found

in indolence, pure indolence,
an ocean of darkness,

in silence, an arm of the moon,
a hand that enters slowly.
*
I am reminded of a story
Camus tells, of a man in prison camp.

He had carved a piano keyboard
with a nail on a piece of wood.

And sat there playing the piano.
This music was made entirely of silence.

LOUIS SIMPSON

Why They Stopped Singing

They stopped singing because
They remembered why they had started

Stopped because
They were singing too well

When they stopped they hoped for
A silence to listen into.

Had they sung longer
The people would not have known what to say.

They stopped from the fear
Of singing for ever

They stopped because they saw the rigid world
Become troubled

Saw it begin
Composing a question.

Then they stopped singing
While there was time.

ROY FISHER

Who?

after a while
he began to forget the words
lost the art of conversation
stopped winning friends

that's the way it begins
        with the words

soon his eyes began to set
into their bone horizon
left his face as blank as moon

after the eyes the legs
held muffled conversations with the earth
fell out of step and limped

that's the way it ends
        with the earth

he didn't get about much anymore
his hands fell empty like his head
and everything he did was slow

slower and slower
until one day
he wasn't there at all

MILES GIBSON

Opening The Cage: 14 Variations on 14 Words

I have nothing to say and I am saying it and that is poetry—*John Cage*

I have to say poetry and is that nothing and am I saying it
I am and I have poetry to say and is that nothing saying it
I am nothing and I have poetry to say and that is saying it
I that am saying poetry have nothing and it is I and to say
And I say that I am to have poetry and saying it is nothing
I am poetry and nothing and saying it is to say that I have
To have nothing is poetry and I am saying that and I say it
Poetry is saying I have nothing and I am to say that and it
Saying nothing I am poetry and I have to say that and it is
It is and I am and I have poetry saying say that to nothing
It is saying poetry to nothing and I say I have and am that
Poetry is saying I have it and I am nothing and to say that
And that nothing is poetry I am saying and I have to say it
Saying poetry is nothing and to that I say I am and have it

EDWIN MORGAN

SUGGESTIONS FOR WRITING AND DISCUSSION

1 *Man, Animal, Clock of Blood, Out of Unrest*
   a Why does Anselm Hollo call man 'a beautiful goof'? Suggest specific characteristics and activities in mankind implied by 'the old song in his head', and discuss whether they make life preferable to that lived by 'the animal'.
   b How does *Out of Unrest* develop the ideas of the first poem? What is the significance of its quotation from the philosopher Kierkegaard? What does Anselm Hollo suggest to you when he refers to 'the dark', and Paul Evans in his references to light?
   c It is difficult. There are
        so many people I am,
        obscuring
        the one face I would become
      Write a short story or poem that will illustrate what these lines mean for you and your life, or inspired by the picture.

2 *Prayer Before Birth*
   a Discuss specific examples of the types of experience that are feared here. What do you think is meant by
        tall walls
        wise lies
        a white light in the back of my mind
        the sins that in me the world shall commit
        the parts I must play
        the man . . . who thinks he is God?
      Are there any words you would add to this prayer?

   Narcissus, The Ripples, Passing Through, Mary Mary Magdalene
   b Discuss how these four poems make use of the imagery that appears at the end of Louis MacNeice's poem, and analyse the special meanings that each poem gives it.
   c What does Elizabeth Jennings mean by 'translucence' and 'the crystalline presence' in her poem? Write about one of the 'vivid gazes' in your experience when you were aware of these qualities.
   d Walking together through spaces other people have filled,
      Our edges become hot in the air remembering them
      Write a short story or play that will develop these lines.

3 *Reported Missing, The Worst Of All Loves, Outside the Gates of Eden, At Lunchtime A Story of Love*
   a Write a story or poem about a face that makes you feel 'dissatisfied' with yourself, perhaps based on a similar incident to that described by John Cotton.
   b Discuss the two types of description that conflict in Barry Cole's poem. Is either of them 'truer' than the other?
   c Discuss what you think Roger McGough may have in mind in the last line of his poem.

4 *Parlour-Piece, Hesitant, Incident, The Rag Doll To The Heedless Child*
   a Write a story or poem about someone who wishes to show his love for someone else, yet cannot.
   b Do these poems remind you of situations in novels or films? If so, tell one another about them.

5 *Pomander, Jenny*
   a Can you think of another word like 'Pomander' out of which you can make new combinations of letters and words? Arrange them into a pattern of lines for exhibition. Find examples of concrete and other visual poetry and discuss what their patterns say to you. (Other experiments by Edwin Morgan can be found in *A Second Life*, published by Edinburgh University Press, from which this poem is taken. A computer poem appears in *Dragonsteeth*. See also pages 78 and 85 of this volume.) What is the importance of poetry of this kind?
   b The 'pages' reproduced on p. 22 are from a 'Humament' by Tom Phillips. '. . . a treated work. A Victorian novel (*A Human Document*, by W. H. Mallock, published in 1892) has been taken page by page and altered, adapted and metamorphosed; its text has been excavated for new ambiguities of character and situation and new ironies and paradoxes of utterance.' Discuss what you find here. How is this like the technique of collage, and what is the purpose of that means of artistic expression?
   c Finally on the following page is a poem by Allen Fisher. The 'instructions' he gives are 'Read in any/every direction. Two or more voices can read in different directions simultaneously.' Try it out and discuss the results.

```
PeReS i
oSePeR
T i FoNe
eN i ToF
ReSeP i
oPeReS
F i NoTe
eT i FoN
```

6 *First Love, Seascape, This Day, The Love Day*
   a Discuss the different moods and views of falling in love presented in these poems, and compare them with other situations you have encountered in stories and films. Are any more 'true to life' than others?

7 *Rupert Hears Gruff Voices*
   a Discuss why the poet has used this particular layout and what it contributes to the meaning of the poem. Is there anything similar here to the features you discussed in 5, particularly section b? Do you agree with either 'side presented'?
   b Build up a poem based on different people's reactions to the same event—e.g., a christening or funeral/accident/crime. Perhaps this could grow out of an improvised drama session in which different people can imagine the different reactions to these situations.

8 *The Whitsun Weddings*
   a Discuss what feelings emerge through the details of the scenes Philip Larkin notes and the words he uses to describe them.
   b 'loaded with the sum of all they saw': discuss the different viewpoints of the children, fathers, and women as presented here. Are they the same as those you have noticed in people attending weddings?
   c Write a story about a time when you were travelling alone and noticed people, both individuals and groups, who were strangers to you, involved in activities that made you curious about them and their lives.
   d *Anemones for Miss Austen*
      'And they married and lived happily ever after' . . . Should stories, films, plays end like Jane Austen's novels, or do you share the poet's view? Are there endings (happy or unhappy) in life? Should there be in fiction? Discuss novels and films that strike you as being particularly 'realistic' in their 'endings' and in their treatment of marriage.
   e *As Others See Us*
      Read *Breakfast* by Jacques Prévert, *Her Husband* by Ted Hughes, and *My Face Is My Own I Thought* by Tom Raworth (see below). Discuss the relevance of the situations they describe to the last stanza of Jon Stallworthy's poem.

9 *Horoscope, Love Poem, Absence, Love Poem, At Night*
   a   and the surface of every minute
          is a swinging image of you
      Write a poem about someone whose absence you feel keenly.

10 *Telescope*
   a How does this poem develop the idea of *The Ripples* by David Sutton? (p. 11).
   b Lee Harwood, referring to his poetry, writes:
      'The poem is always unfinished and only complete (and then in only one way) when read by someone else. I mean a work of art which only achieves wholeness when an audience is present . . . The important telegram torn in half and only one half given to the reader to fill in the missing half. That's what my poems are about. The reader fills in the blanks with his own memories and imaginations so each reader creates a different poem from the basic foundations the writer gives him.'
      Discuss the relevance of this statement to the other poems you have read in this anthology, and to other forms of art—paintings and sculpture, plays, novels, music.
   c Write a piece in which you 'fill in the missing half' of Lee Harwood's poem.

11 *Travelling Between Places, The Lane, When You Go, You Become A Star*
   a Write about an experience that any of these poems brings to your memory.
   b Discuss the effects of the layout of Lee Harwood's poem and compare it with the page from *A Humament* (see 5b above and p. 22).

12 *At Four O'Clock In The Morning*
   a 'As all is temporary and is changeable'—do you agree with the feelings expressed in this poem, in relation to other aspects of living as well?
   Touch, Bodies, Somewhere I have Never Travelled, Gladly Beyond
   b Study the technique of these poems, their rhythms and the arrangement of sounds and lines : how do they enact the physical sensations they describe so that in your imagination you can feel them too?

13 *Part of Plenty, The Wife's Tale, Trio, Happiness*
   Write about an occasion when you have been keenly aware of the feeling of joy or contentment.

14 *Men of Terry Street, Morning Song, Human Affection, At Seven A Son, Prayer, Rising Five, Mirror*
   a Discuss what is similar and what is different in the poets' feelings towards their children in these poems.
   b Why does Sylvia Plath refer to 'a drafty museum' in *Morning Song*? Is there any connection between 'your nakedness shadows our safety' and 'the darker face behind the mirror' referred to by David Wevill? Discuss how *Mirror*, also by Sylvia Plath, and *Rising Five* develop the final part of David Wevill's *Prayer*.
   c Compare the *Prayer* of David Wevill with Louis MacNeice's *Prayer Before Birth*.
   d Discuss what changes you see in the faces of the same person painted by Rembrandt—all self-portraits, in fact.

15 *Old Woman, Grandfather, Two Grandad Poems, Two Clocks, Old Men, The Patricians, My Grandmother*
   a Discuss what the poets admire in the old people written about here. What other feelings and attitudes emerge?
   b Discuss what
         the inheritance of the oldest, a right to power
      and
            their disenchantments
         Settle around me like a cold fog

(lines from *The Patricians*) mean to you as you think of old people you know.
   c Compare the two poems by Elizabeth Jennings. Could they have been written about the same person?
   d Compare how *Two Clocks* and *My Grandmother* use objects to convey the feelings you have analysed in (a).
   e Write a poem about your feelings towards an old person you know well.

16 *The Hospital in Winter, Visiting Hour*
   a Write about memories stirred in you by these poems, either of visiting a patient in hospital or staying there yourself.

17 *Grave By A Holm-Oak, Memorial, With Decorum, The Old Women, Mrs Root*
   a Discuss the attitudes towards death that emerge in these poems. Do you know of people like Mrs Root and the 'terrible hags' of George Mackay Brown's poem? If so, what are your feelings towards them? Are you shocked by D. M. Black's poem (compare it with Dylan Thomas's *Do Not Go Gentle Into That Goodnight*) or do you think its attitude healthy? (It would be interesting to compare the differences between various societies' behaviour at funerals in this connection.)
   b Write about a family at a funeral, and the attitudes of the people present.

18 *Poor Women In A City Church, An Arundel Tomb*
   a Discuss the ways in which Philip Larkin suggests the passing of time in this poem.
   b What is 'the attitude that remains' in the tomb? Does it offer any hope for mankind?
   c What comfort do you imagine the poor women in Seamus Heaney's poem gain from their attendances at the city church? *Here*
   d R. S. Thomas, besides being a poet, is a priest working in Wales. Have you read the sonnets of another priest, G. M. Hopkins? How do they develop
         It is too late to start
         For destinations not of the heart
         I must stay here with my hurt
      Is it? Must you?
   e What do you think is being referred to in the 3rd and 4th Stanzas of *Here*?
   f   I am like a tree:
         From my top boughs I can see
         The footprints that lead up to me
      Find and read again other poems in this anthology that are concerned with this idea.

g   Does religion have any meaning in the twentieth century?

19 *A Small Consolation, Oblivion, Do Not Go Gentle Into That Good-night*
   a   Does any of these poems echo your own feelings about the prospect of growing old and dying? Either write your own poem about your thoughts of the future, or a short story in which you imagine yourself to be one of the people whose thoughts are described in these poems, revealing the situation that has caused him to feel in this way.

20 *In The Night, The Secret Sharer, Counting The Beats*
   a   Write a poem called 'Night Thoughts' about your feelings as you lie awake at night.

21 *First, Goodbye, Song, Your Cry, The Feel of Hands*
   a   Write a play or short story based on your reading of these poems, or on the pictures that accompany them.

22 *One Flesh, Old Couple, The Sea Widow, On A Summer Night*
   a   Discuss how these poems echo or contrast with poems that you have read and discussed that are placed earlier in this anthology.

23 *A Dream of Hanging, At The Florist's, The Stranger, The Suspect*
   a   Do these poems remind you of nightmares you have experienced? If so describe them for others to hear or read.
   b   Improvise a play based on *The Suspect*, and then imagine similar nightmarish situations.
   c   *The Beast*
      Write a poem or story about when you have been aware of yourself externally and objectively
                 . . . this creature
      at last come home to me

24 *Report on August, Song*
   a   Discuss the 'accusations small but just' that could be made about the lives of the people you live and work with, your neighbours and friends, yourselves. Read *The Waste Land* by T. S. Eliot: is his vision of society in the 1920s still relevant 50 years later?

25 *My Face Is My Own, I Thought, Her Husband, Breakfast, Ghosts*
   a   Describe an incident like those depicted in the poems here—a rift between two people. Don't make any comment, but, either like Jacques Prévert let a character speak, or like Ted Hughes and Tom Raworth let the reported actions of the people speak for themselves.
   b   Now use this poem you have written as the starting-point for a story or play developing the situation more fully, or write one to illustrate the final two lines of *Ghosts*.

   c   *Road Song, Lonely Man*
      Write about an occasion like that described by Brian Patten, when you only had your 'gawky shadow' for company or about the shadows that form the subject of Denise Levertov's poem.

26 a   *Mr Bleaney*
      Discuss the narrator's attitude towards Mr Bleaney, and by implication towards himself.
   b   *An Irish Monk on Lindisfarne About 650 A.D.*
      What is similar about the situation of this person to that described in Philip Larkin's poem? What do you think his encounter with the Pict woman has taught him? Discuss what you think to be the meaning of the gulls' cry and the bell's reply, and of the poem's last three lines.
   c   *The Last of the Peasantry*
      Compare this poem with *Here* (page 55), also by R. S. Thomas.
   d   *Moving Through The Silent Crowd*
      This poem refers to the years of the Depression in the '30s. Is this picture still relevant today?
   e   I'm haunted by these images,
      I'm haunted by their emptiness
      Discuss other twentieth century literature that is 'haunted' in this sense. How does it contribute to our understanding of contemporary social problems? What are the images that 'haunt' you?

27 *Toyland*
   a   Why has Roy Fisher given his poem this title? Paint your picture of your familiar scene: do you view it in the same light as he does?
   Thinks, South London Prose Poem, No Place, Well It Has Been A Pleasure England
   b   Discuss how these poems develop and comment on the situation described in *Toyland*. Are there any aspects that you recognise in the scene around you?

28 *Good Friday*
   Use this poem as the basis for a wider discussion of
   a   the meaning of 'Christ' in our society.
   b   the purpose and effectiveness of being 'an educatit man'.

29 *Postcard, The Slow Starter, Poem, Who?*
   a   Discuss what fundamental criticisms of our lives are made by these poems, and give details of the reasons you find in your experience for their being made.

b   Improvise or write a play called *The Slow Starter* based on the ideas in Louis MacNeice's poem.

c   Write your poem about what you find lacking in the society in which you live: have you an answer? Have any of the poems included in this anthology?

30   *Will It Be So Again?, Your Attention Please*

a   *Will* it be so again?

b   Discuss your reactions to Peter Porter's poem. What do you think his attitude is towards the subject he describes? What is the tone of his poem? Is that of Edwin Brock's the same?

Five Ways to Kill A Man

c   Do you agree with the conclusion of this poem?

The Silent Piano

d   Discuss the meaning of this poem. Where is 'the inner life' to be found? What is the importance of the final image?

Why They Stopped Singing

e   What do you think is the 'question' that lurks behind this poem?

SUGGESTIONS FOR FURTHER READING

Patricia Beer	*The Loss of the Magyar*—Longman
	The Survivors—Longman
	Just Like The Resurrection—Macmillan
	The Estuary—Macmillan
	Mrs Beer's House (autobiography)—Macmillan
D. M. Black	*With Decorum*—Scorpion Press
	Theory of Diet—Turret Books
	The Educators—Barrie & Rockliff
	A selection of his poems is included in *Penguin Modern Poets 11*
Edwin Brock	*A Family Affair*—Scorpion Press
	An Attempt at Exorcism—Scorpion Press
	With Love From Judas—Scorpion Press
	A selection of his poems is included in *Penguin Modern Poets 8*
George Mackay Brown	*Poems New and Selected*—The Hogarth Press
	A selection of his poems is included in *Penguin Modern Poems 21*
Charles Causley	*Union Street*—Hart-Davis
	Johnny Allelulia—Hart-Davis
	Underneath the Water—Macmillan
	Figure of Eight—Macmillan
	A selection of his poems is included in *Penguin Modern Poets 3*
Barry Cole	*Moonsearch*—Methuen
	Blood Ties—Turret Books
	Ulysses in the Town of Coloured Glass—Turret Books
Tony Connor	*With Love Somehow*—Oxford University Press
	Lodgers—Oxford University Press
	Kon in Springtime—Oxford University Press
	In the Happy Valley—Oxford University Press
John Cotton	*Poetry Introduction I*—Faber
	Old Movies—Hogarth Press
e.e.cummings	*Selected Poems*—Penguin
John Daniel	*Poetry Introduction I*—Faber
Douglas Dunn	*Terry Street*—Faber
	A Happier Life—Faber
Paul Evans	*February*—Fulcrum Press
Elaine Feinstein	*Poetry Introduction I*—Faber
Roy Fisher	*Collected Poems*—Fulcrum Press
	The Cut Pages—Fulcrum Press
Miles Gibson	*The Guilty Bystander*—Methuen
Robert Graves	*Selected Poems*—Penguin
Thom Gunn	*Fighting Terms*—Faber
	The Sense of Movement—Faber
	My Sad Captains—Faber
	Positives—Faber
	Touch—Faber
	Moly—Faber
Ian Hamilton	*Poetry Introduction I*—Faber
David Harsent	*Poetry Introduction I*—Faber
Lee Harwood	*The White Room*—Fulcrum Press
	Landscapes—Fulcrum Press
	The Sinking Colony—Fulcrum Press
	A selection of his poems is included in *Penguin Modern Poets 19*

Seamus Heaney	*Death of A Naturalist*—Faber	Peter Porter	*Once Bitten, Twice Bitten*—Scorpion Press
	Door Into The Dark—Faber		*Poems Ancient and Modern*—Scorpion Press
	Wintering Out—Faber		*A Porter Folio*—Scorpion Press
Anselm Hollo	*And It's A Song*—Migrant Press		A selection of his poems is included in *Penguin*
	The Coherences—Trigram		*Modern Poets 2*
	Faces and Forms—Ambit	Jacques Prévert	*Penguin Modern European Poets* selection
	Children of Albion (ed. Horovitz)—Penguin	Tom Raworth	*The Relation Ship*—Cape
Frances Horovitz	*Children of Albion* (ed. Horovitz)—Penguin		*The Big Green Day*—Trigram Press
Ted Hughes	*The Hawk in the Rain*—Faber		*Lion Lion*—Trigram Press
	Lupercal—Faber		A selection of his poems is included in *Penguin*
	Wodwo—Faber		*Modern Poets 19*
	Crow—Faber	Carl Sandburg	*Collected Poems*—Harcourt, Brace & World
Elizabeth Jennings	*Collected Poems 1967*—Macmillan		Inc
	The Animals' Arrival—Macmillan	Louis Simpson	*Selected Poems*—Oxford University Press
	Lucidities—Macmillan	John Smith	*Excursus in Autumn*—Hutchinson
	A selection of her poems is included in *Penguin*		*A Discreet Immorality*—Hart-Davis
	Modern Poets 1	Stevie Smith	*Selected Poems*—Longman
Brian Jones	*A Family Album*—Alan Ross		*The Frog Prince*—Longman
	Interiors—Alan Ross		*Scorpion*—Longman
Philip Larkin	*The North Ship*—Faber		A selection of her poems appears in *Penguin*
	The Whitsun Weddings—Faber		*Modern Poems 8*
Laurie Lee	*Collected Poems*—Studio Vista	Bernard Spencer	*Collected Poems*—Alan Ross
Denise Levertov	*The Jacob's Ladder*—Cape	Stephen Spender	*Collected Poems*—Faber
	A selection of her poems is included in *Penguin*	Jon Stallworthy	*The Astronomy of Love*—Oxford University
	Modern Poets 9		Press
C. Day-Lewis	*Selected Poems*—Penguin		*Out of Bounds*—Oxford University Press
Norman MacCaig	*Collected Poems*—The Hogarth Press		*Root and Branch*—Chatto & Windus
	A selection of his poems is included in *Penguin*	David Sutton	*Out On A Limb*—Rapp & Whiting
	Modern Poets 21	Dylan Thomas	*Collected Poems*—Dent
Louis MacNeice	*Collected Poems*—Faber	R. S. Thomas	*Song At The Year's Turning*—Hart-Davis
Derek Mahon	*Night Crossing*—Oxford University Press		*Poetry for Supper*—Hart-Davis
Roger McGough	*The Mersey Sound*—Penguin		*Tares*—Hart-Davis
	Watchwords—Cape		*The Bread of Truth*—Hart-Davis
	Frinck and Summer With Monica—Michael		*Pièta*—Hart-Davis
	Joseph		*Not That He Brought Flowers*—Hart-Davis
	After The Merrymaking—Cape		A selection of his poems appears in *Penguin*
Edwin Morgan	*The Second Life*—Edinburgh University Press		*Modern Poets I*
Norman Nicholson	*Collected Poems*—Faber	Chris Torrance	*Green, Orange, Purple, Red*—Ferry Press
Brian Patten	*Little Johnny's Confessions*—Allen & Unwin	Gael Turnbull	*A Trampoline*—Cape Goliard
	Notes to the Hurrying Man—Allen & Unwin	Ted Walker	*The Fox On The Barn Door*—Cape
	The Irrelevant Song—Allen & Unwin		*The Solitaries*—Cape
Sylvia Plath	*Ariel*—Faber		*The Night Bathers*—Cape
	Crossing The Water—Faber	David Wevill	*Birth of A Shark*—Macmillan
	Winter Trees—Faber		*Christ of the Ice-Floes*—Macmillan
	The Colossus—Faber		*Firebreak*—Macmillan

ACKNOWLEDGEMENTS

The Publisher's thanks are due to the following for permission to use copyright poems:

Macmillan & Co. Ltd for David Wevill's 'Prayer', 'Memorial' and 'Poem' from *Firebreak*, Elizabeth Jennings's 'My Grandmother' and 'One Flesh' from *Collected Poems*, Patricia Beer's 'A Dream of Hanging' and 'Postcard' from *Just Like the Resurrection*, Bernard Bergonzi for 'Anemones for Miss Austen'; Scorpion Press for Peter Porter's 'Your Attention Please', D. M. Black's 'With Decorum' and Edwin Brock's 'Five Ways to Kill a Man'; The Hogarth Press for G. M. Brown's 'The Old Women' from *Poems New and Selected*; The Poetry Society for Charles Causley's 'Mary, Mary Magdalene', Tom Phillips's 'A Humament', Maurice Cockrill's 'Rupert Hears Rough Voices', Roger McGough's 'Two Grandad Poems': 'Bucket' and 'Railings'; Peter Finch for 'Rock 'n Roll Poem' and Gerald Ashby's 'Jenny' from *Poetry Review Summer 1970* and *Spring 1971*; Methuen & Co. Ltd for Barry Cole's 'Reported Missing' from *The Visitors* and Miles Gibson's 'Thinks' and 'Who?' from *The Guilty Bystander*; Oxford University Press for Derek Mahon's 'Grandfather' from *Night-Crossing*, Louis Simpson's 'The Silent Piano' from *Adventures of the Letter I*, Tony Connor's 'Old Man' and 'Mrs Root' from *In the Happy Valley* and 'On a Summer Night' from *With Love Somehow*; John Cotton for 'Outside the Gates of Eden'; Harcourt Brace Jovanovich Inc. for e. e. cummings's 'somewhere i have never travelled' © 1931, 1959 by e. e. cummings, Reprinted from *Complete Poems* 1913 to 1962; John Daniel for 'Two Clocks' and 'No Place'; Faber & Faber Ltd for Douglas Dunn's 'Passing Through', 'The Love Day', 'Love Poem', 'The Worst of All Loves', 'Men of Terry Street' and 'The Patricians' from *Terry Street*, Louis MacNeice's 'Prayer Before Birth' and 'The Slow Starter' from *The Collected Poems of Louis MacNeice*, Ted Hughes's 'Parlour-Piece' and 'Song' from *The Hawk in the Rain* and 'Her Husband' from *Wodwo*; Thom Gunn for 'Touch' from *Touch*. 'The Secret Sharer' from *Fighting Terms* and 'The Feel of Hands' from *My Sad Captains*; Seamus Heaney's 'The Wife's Tale' from *Door Into the Dark* and 'Poor Women in a City Church' from *Death of a Naturalist*; Norman Nicholson's 'Rising Five' from *The Pot Geranium*, Philip Larkin's 'An Arundel Tomb', 'Mr Bleaney' and 'The Whitsun Weddings' from *The Whitsun Weddings*, Stephen Spender's 'Moving through the Silent Crowd' from *Collected Poems of Stephen Spender* and Ian Hamilton's 'Your Cry' from *The Visit*; Elaine Feinstein for 'At Seven a Son' and 'Bodies'; *Poetry Review* for Alan Fisher's poem; Fulcrum Press for Paul Evans's

'Out of Unrest' from *February*, © Paul Evans, Lee Harwood's 'You Become a Star' and 'Telescope' from *Landscapes*, © Lee Harwood and Roy Fisher's 'The Hospital in Winter', 'Report on August', 'Toyland' and 'Why they stopped Singing' from *Collected Poems*, © Roy Fisher; Mr Robert Graves and Cassell & Co. Ltd for 'Counting the Beats' from *Collected Poems 1965*; David Harsent for 'The Rag Doll to the Heedless Child'; Jonathan Cape Ltd for Anselm Hollo's 'Man, Animal, Clock of Blood' from *Maya*, Tom Raworth's 'My Face is My Own, I Thought' from *The Relation Ship* and Gael Turnbull's 'An Irish Monk on Lindisfarne—About 650 A.D.' from *A Trampoline*; Anselm Hollo for 'Well it has been a Pleasure England'; Frances Horowitz for 'Love Poem'; Elizabeth Jennings for 'Narcissus' and 'Ghosts'; André Deutsch Ltd for Elizabeth Jennings's 'Absence' and 'Old Woman' from *A Sense of the World* and 'In the Night' from *A Way of Looking*; Brian Jones for 'The Lane'; Jonathan Cape Ltd and the Executors of the Estate of C. Day Lewis 'Will It Be So Again?' from *Collected Poems 1954*; Roger McGough's 'The Stranger' from *Watchwords* and Ted Walker's 'Old Couple' from *Fox on a Barn Door*; The Hogarth Press for Laurie Lee's 'At Night' from *The Sun My Monument*; Laurie Lee for 'First Love'; Jonathan Cape Ltd for Denise Levertov's 'Lonely Man' from *The Jacob's Ladder*; Edinburgh University Press, for Edwin Morgan's 'Pomander', 'When You Go', 'Trio', 'The Suspect', 'Good Friday' and 'Opening the Cage' from *The Second Life*; Norman MacCaig for 'Incident' and 'The Visiting Hour'; Hope Leresche & Steele and Penguin Books Ltd for Roger McGough's 'At Lunchtime A Story of Love' from *Penguin Modern Poets 10*; George Allen & Unwin Ltd for Brian Patten's 'Travelling Between Places', 'Seascape', 'The Beast' from *Little Johnny's Confession* and 'Hesitant', 'At Four O'clock in the Morning' and 'The Road Song' from *The Irrelevant Song*; Olwyn Hughes for Sylvia Plath's 'Morning Song' from *Ariel*, © Ted Hughes 1965 and 'Mirror' from *Crossing the Water*, © Ted Hughes 1971; City Lights Books for Jacques Prévert's 'At the Florist's', 'Song' and 'Breakfast' from *Paroles*, trans. Ferlinghetti, © Les Editions de Point du Jour, Paris, 1947; Carl Sandburg's 'Happiness' from *Chicago Poems* by Carl Sandburg, © 1916 by Holt, Rinehart and Winston, Inc., © 1944 by Carl Sandburg. Reprinted by permission of Harcourt Brace Jovanovich Inc.; Rupert Hart-Davis for John Smith's 'A Small Consolation' and 'First Good-bye'; Longman Group Ltd for Stevie Smith's 'Grave by a Holm-Oak', 'Oblivion', 'Human Affection' and 'The Sea Widow' from *Scorpion*; London Magazine for Bernard Spencer's 'Party of Plenty'; Chatto & Windus Ltd for Jon Stallworthy's 'As

Others See Us' from *Root and Branch*; André Deutsch Ltd for David Sutton's 'The Ripples' from *Out on a Limb*; J. M. Dent & Sons Ltd and the Trustees for the Copyrights of the late Dylan Thomas for 'Do Not Go Gentle . . .' from *Collected Poems of Dylan Thomas*; Rupert Hart-Davis for R. S. Thomas's 'Here' from *Tares* and 'The Last of the Peasantry' from *Song At the Year's Turning* and the Ferry Press for Chris Torrance's 'South London Prose Poem'.

We would also like to thank the following for permission to reprint copyright photographs (page numbers in brackets) :

J. Allan Cash (11, 37, 52, 79, 82–3) ; Barnaby's Picture Library (27) ; Camera Press Agency (39, 48, 49, 54) ; Bob Collins (12, 16, 17, 40, 47, 51, 55, 57, 69, 74) ; Greater London Council, Trustees of the Iveagh Bequest, Kenwood (44 *left*) ; Hammer Film Production Ltd. (64) ; Sarah Hobson (29) ; Noeline Kelly (32–3) ; Kunsthistorisches Museum (43 *right*) ; Christopher Lukas (18–19, 28) ; MGM–EMI (24) ; Richard Murby (59) ; Museum of Modern Art, New York (80) ; National Gallery (15, 42, 44 *right*, 45) ; National Gallery of Art, Washington, DC (43 *left*) ; Radio Times Hulton Picture Library (72) ; The Solomon R. Guggenheim Museum (66) ; Spectrum (26) ; The Tate Gallery (2, 9, 35, 62, 77) ; Laurence Whistler (10). The painting on the half title is reproduced by courtesy of the Edward James Foundation.

INDEX